GUIDEBOOK

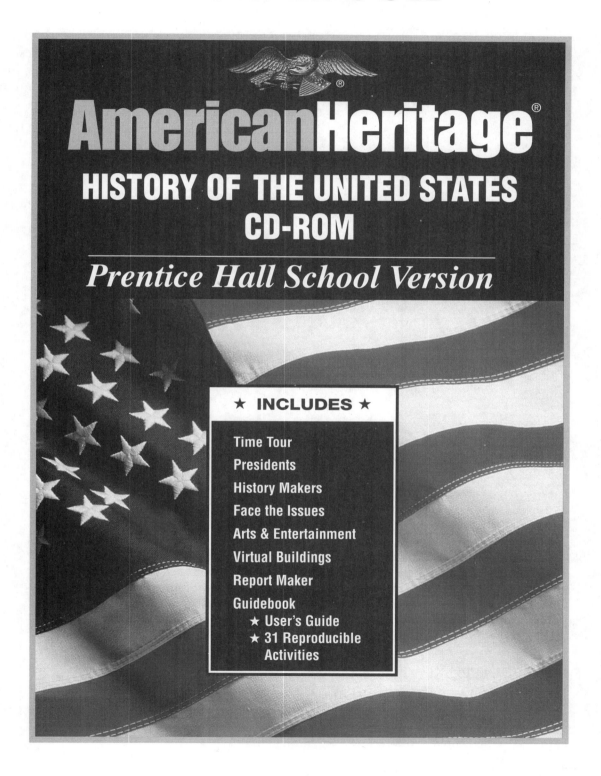

AmericanHeritage®

HISTORY OF THE UNITED STATES
CD-ROM

Prentice Hall School Version

★ **INCLUDES** ★

Time Tour
Presidents
History Makers
Face the Issues
Arts & Entertainment
Virtual Buildings
Report Maker
Guidebook
  ★ User's Guide
  ★ 31 Reproducible
    Activities

PRENTICE HALL
Upper Saddle River, New Jersey
Needham, Massachusetts

ISBN 0-13-427055-X

7 8 9 10 11 12   06 05 04 03 02 01

PRENTICE HALL

Guidebook Contents

Reference Section

Installing and Starting the CD-ROM

SYSTEM REQUIREMENTS
Windows®
- PC with 486DX/66MHz or higher processor (Pentium processor recommended)
- 8 MB RAM (12 MB RAM recommended); 5 MB available hard disk space
- SVGA graphics (256 colors with 640 x 480 resolution)
- Double-speed CD-ROM drive or faster (Quad speed recommended)
- 16-bit sound card
- Mouse or compatible pointing device
- Windows 3.1 or later (Windows 95 recommended)

Macintosh®
- Macintosh or Power Macintosh with a 25MHz/68040 or faster processor
- 13" or larger color monitor (256 colors with 640 x 480 resolution)
- 8 MB RAM; 2 MB available hard disk space
- Double-speed CD-ROM drive or faster
- System 7.0 or later

INSTALLING THE DISC
Windows
1. Start Windows.
2. Insert the *American Heritage® History of the United States* disc into CD-ROM drive.
3. For Windows 3.x, in Windows Program Manager, select Run from the File menu. For Windows 95, click Start, then select Run from the pop-up menu.
4. Type the letter of your CD-ROM drive followed by   :\setup
5. Click OK.

Macintosh
1. Insert the *American Heritage® History of the United States* disc into CD-ROM drive.
2. Click the History of the United States CD-ROM icon on your desktop.
3. Click the Install the History of the United States icon.

STARTING THE DISC
Please note that the *American Heritage® History of the United States* disc must be in your CD-ROM drive for the application to run.

Windows 95
1. Click Start.
2. From the pop-up menu, select Programs; then select BPMC.
3. Highlight and click the History of the United States icon.

Windows 3.x
1. Start Windows.
2. In Windows Program Manager, locate the BPMC program group.
3. Click the History of the United States icon.

Macintosh
1. Locate the History of the United States folder on your hard drive or other location specified during installation.
2. Click the History of the United States icon.

Exiting the Disc
Roll over the pop-up tool bar on the right edge of the screen and click Quit.

User's Guide

★ INTRODUCING THE CD-ROM

The *American Heritage® History of the United States* CD-ROM provides an interactive, multimedia exploration of the American experience. The historical, political, and social aspects of the American story are presented in lively formats that take the user on an electronic journey of learning and discovery.

Combining text, audio, and video, the *American Heritage® History of the United States* CD-ROM is comprehensive, fun, and easy to use. You can brush up on the details of the Constitutional Convention, hear a speech by Franklin Roosevelt, walk through a Victorian home, or listen to a debate on child labor. When you are done, you can create an on-screen presentation or print a report about what you have seen and heard. All the while, the latest in CD-ROM technology allows you to navigate through interactive areas at the click of a mouse.

Seven Stations   The *American Heritage® History of the United States* CD-ROM opens in an imaginary Time Capsule. The Time Capsule has seven stations:

- **Time Tour**
- **Presidents**
- **History Makers**
- **Face the Issues**
- **Library**
- **Arts and Entertainment**
- **Virtual Buildings**

Detailed descriptions of each station, as well as of the Time Capsule, and instructions for navigating them appear on the pages that follow. A chart showing the CD-ROM contents is on pages 18–19.

★ NAVIGATING THE CD-ROM

Finding your way around the *American Heritage® History of the United States* CD-ROM is easy and fun. To access any section, simply click the icon that represents it. The name of the section appears as you roll your cursor over the icon. Or you may select a section from a scroll-out table of contents.

Each section includes scrollable text and images. These images and the captions describing them automatically change as the text is scrolled. The appearance of video control buttons as you scroll through the text indicates that a video is available. Click the play button to start the video.

Hot spots, indicated by colored text, signal links to other material on the CD-ROM. Click red hot spots to bring up a menu of additional references to the highlighted topic. Click the items in the menu to access a particular topic. Blue hot spots signal that an audio recording is available. Click the blue hot spot to bring up an audio box, and use the control buttons to start and stop the recording. The presence of a chart or map is signaled by a chart/map icon in the margin next to the text. Click the icon to see the graphic.

To help you move through the CD-ROM, there are two scroll-out menus, at the right and left of each screen. These menus appear when you roll your cursor over the margins at either side of the screen.

The **left scroll-out menu** lists the main sections on the CD-ROM, including the Time Capsule. (See below.) When you click the section name, a submenu appears. For example, clicking History Makers brings up a submenu listing the people profiled in that section. Clicking the name of an individual History Maker will bring you directly to that person's biography.

Roll your cursor over the left edge of the screen to bring up a menu of the sections of the CD-Rom.

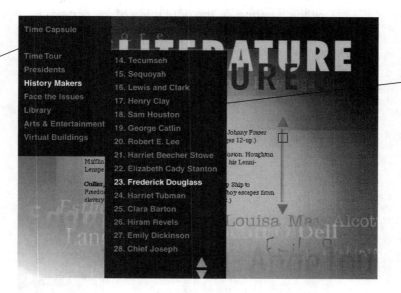

Click the section name to bring up a submenu of the section contents.

The **right scroll-out menu** provides tools to help you navigate the section you are in. (See below.) It also provides access to global controls used to navigate between sections.

★ Section Controls

Click **Previous** to go to the screen that precedes the one you are viewing.

Click **Next** to turn the "page." This takes you to the next screen.

Click **Back** to go to the opening screen of the section you are currently exploring.

★ Global Controls

Retrace takes you to the last screen you were viewing. For example, if you are viewing the biography of George Washington in the Presidents of the United States section, and then go to the Time Tour, clicking Retrace will take you back to the Washington biography. You can retrace your steps up to ten screens.

Click **Index** to access a scrollable index of the entire CD-ROM. Click a specific Index entry to go to that topic.

Click **Notebook** to access a special text box in which you can take notes as you use the CD-ROM. You can also paste selections of text from the CD-ROM into the Notebook. For information on how to use your notes as you create reports, see the Report Maker section in the instructions for the Library on page 15.

Click **Help** to bring up a sample screen with detailed instructions about the current section. Clicking active areas of the sample screen will call up related text that explains how the section works

Click **Quit** to end your CD-ROM exploration session.

Roll the cursor over the right edge of the screen to bring up section and global controls.

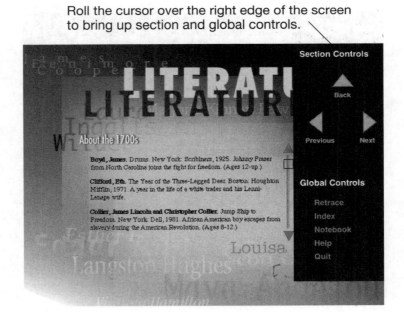

★ **TIME CAPSULE**

You begin your electronic journey through American history by entering a Time Capsule. It is designed as your home base while you explore the CD-ROM. A pair of video hosts, Freddie and Zoe, appear at the beginning to help you along. (Once you get to know the Time Capsule environment, you can click once to leave your hosts behind and continue exploring on your own.)

Walking Around the Time Capsule

The Time Capsule has seven stations, each representing a section of the CD-ROM. The Time Capsule opens at the Time Tour station. (See below.) You can walk around the Time Capsule by clicking the right or left edges of the screen. Each click brings you to the next station. To help you keep your bearings, the stations to the right or left of the one where you are standing are partially visible. The name of the station appears as you roll your cursor over it.

When you arrive in the Time Capsule,
you find yourself in front of the Time Tour.

On your left, you can see
the Virtual Buildings station.

On your right, you can
see the Presidents station.

★ TIME TOUR

The Time Tour is an interactive edition of Prentice Hall's *The American Nation*. Scrollable text is accompanied by audio boxes and a variety of images, including fine art, photos, moving footage, maps, charts, and graphs.

At the Time Tour station in the Time Capsule, you will see a collage of nine historical paintings or photographs. (See the picture on page 9.) Each image represents one of the nine units into which the Time Tour is divided. These units correspond to the units in *The American Nation*. By clicking the wall of pictures, you can "step closer" for a better look at each picture. If you roll your cursor over a picture, it will highlight and the unit title will appear on-screen. Click the picture and you'll find yourself on the opening screen of the unit you have chosen.

Taking the Time Tour After you open a unit, a new collage with pictures representing the chapters in the unit appears. Once again, roll over the pictures to bring up the chapter titles. Click a picture to go to that chapter. (Remember, you can also access any of the units or chapters by using the left scroll-out menu.)

On the Time Tour, each screen has a block of scrollable text. (See the typical chapter screen below.) You can scroll through one chapter at a time. Keep an eye out for the videos, audio recordings, maps, and charts that accompany the text.

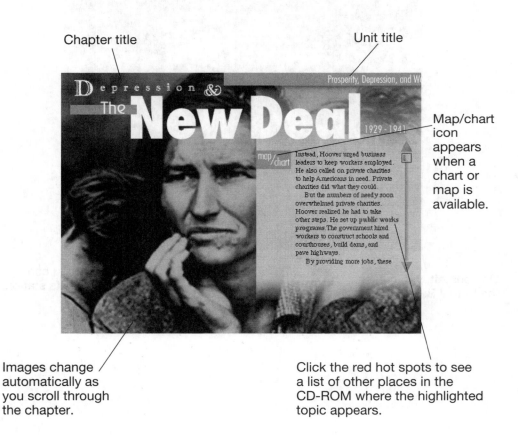

Chapter title

Unit title

Map/chart icon appears when a chart or map is available.

Images change automatically as you scroll through the chapter.

Click the red hot spots to see a list of other places in the CD-ROM where the highlighted topic appears.

★ PRESIDENTS

An attractive stamp album in the Time Capsule is the gateway to biographical multimedia portraits of the Presidents of the United States. Click the album to meet the Presidents.

Meeting the Presidents   Click the album to go to the first screen of the Presidents section. The pages of the album have five or six stamps with pictures of the presidents. The Presidents are listed in chronological order on the page. Click the President's stamp or name to go to his biography. Click "Next" in the right scroll-out menu to turn to the next page of the stamp album.

In this section, scrollable text presents a biography and a description of the President's accomplishments. The text is accompanied by a variety of images. Special controls allow you to play videos. Blue and red hot spots provide access to additional references or bring up an audio box. Rolling over the stamp at the top of a President's screen will bring up the word "Facts." Click to see a window with basic facts about the President.

Roll over the stamp and click "FACTS" to bring up a handy fact sheet about the President.

Click the blue hot spot to hear an audio recording.

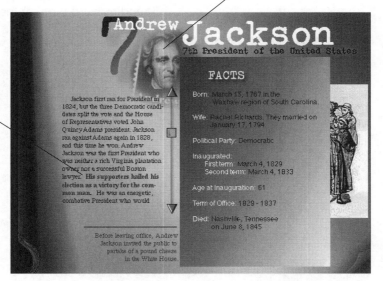

★ HISTORY MAKERS

History Makers presents profiles of a diverse group of 50 individuals who have influenced American history. The History Makers station is represented in the Time Capsule by a group portrait of the History Makers, in chronological order. The portrait is divided into two groups of 25 History Makers each. Clicking once activates the left side. Once the screen is active, roll over an individual's picture to highlight it and bring up the History Maker's name. Then click the highlighted picture to access the History Maker's biography. (See below.)

To activate the right side of the portrait, roll the cursor to the right until it changes to a right arrow. Then click to activate that portion of the History Makers screen. You may also access specific History Makers from a complete listing in the left scroll-out menu.

Learning About the History Makers   Each History Maker biography is devoted to a man or woman who made a significant contribution to American history. Scrollable text blocks, accompanied by a variety of images, provide biographical information and historical accomplishments. Remember to look for the stop and play buttons that indicate the presence of a video clip. Also, watch for blue hot spots, indicating the presence of an audio recording, and red hot spots, indicating additional references to a topic or a glossary definition.

Use the scroll button to go back and forward through the text.

Click the right scroll-out menu to open the Notebook. Highlight and paste text from the CD-ROM into the Notebook.

★ FACE THE ISSUES

Face the Issues explores six issues that helped define the American experience. At the Face the Issues station in the Time Capsule, you will find a cabinet with six compartments. Click to step closer and you will see a picture in each compartment that represents an issue. Click the picture to "face the issue."

Facing the Issues   Each Face the Issues feature is divided into six segments: Background, The Issue, Who Decides, What People Said, Possible Decisions & Consequences, and What Really Happened. Click the submenu at the bottom of each screen to move between the segments. On each screen, scroll through the text and study the images. In What People Said, click the blue hot spots to hear people speak about the issue. In Possible Decisions & Consequences, click each decision on the left to call up a text box that describes the consequences of the decision.

Click a Possible Decision to bring up a scrollable text boxing showing its Possible Consequences.

Click a submenu to move between segments of Face the Issues.

★ LIBRARY

The Library includes bibliographical material, maps of the United States, and the complete texts of the Declaration of Independence and the U.S. Constitution. Also accessible through the library is the Report Maker, which you can use to create on-screen presentations.

Exploring the Library   The Library station in the Time Capsule is represented by a desk with a laptop computer and a pile of books and documents. A wall map hangs behind the desk. Click to step forward for a closer look at the items on the desk. Then click the item of your choice to go to the part of the Library that it represents.

- The **books** on the desk are labeled History, Literature, and Biography. Click a book to access a detailed reading list for that subject area.

- The **documents** on the desk are the Declaration of Independence and the U.S. Constitution. Click to bring up a scrollable copy of the document.

- Clicking the **map** behind the desk will provide you with a choice of three maps of the United States: satellite, political, or physical. Click the button to select the map you would like to view.

Report Maker   The laptop computer on the desk represents a very special feature of the CD-ROM: the Report Maker. The Report Maker allows you to create your own on-screen presentations, or create reports that you can save to your hard drive and print. For on-screen presentations, you can make use of a library of about 200 images from American history.

Click "Report Maker" in the Library to bring up this feature.

Write directly in the Report Maker. You can also open the Note-book and paste text into your report.

Attach pictures from the Image Library to your report. Find an image, highlight the text in the writing area, and click "attach image."

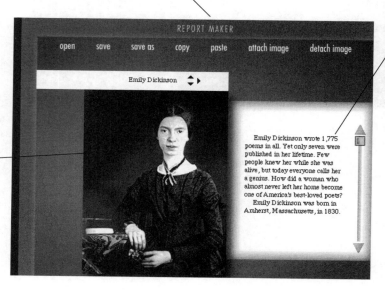

The Report Maker consists of a text box and a media window. (See page 14.) Click Edit Text and you can type as you would in any word processor. Click View Images to access the image library. To attach an image, highlight the text in Edit Text, and then in View Images choose the image and click "attach image." Click Present Report to show the text with the images.

You can also consult your Notebook while in the Report Maker. Use the right scroll-out menu to bring up the Notebook. This allows you to use your notes and selected text from the CD-ROM while you are writing your report. You can even paste text from the Notebook into the Report Maker.

ARTS AND ENTERTAINMENT

★ The cultural side of American life is explored in Arts and Entertainment. Emphasis is on books, music, sports, television, and movies.

In the Time Capsule, the Arts and Entertainment section is represented by a stack of books, a phonograph, a collection of sports trophies, a movie camera, and a television. Rolling over the objects brings up the name of the section: Books, Music, Sports, TV, and Movies. Click to enter the world of American arts and entertainment.

The five sections of Arts and Entertainment function in the same way as the Time Tour. Scrollable text blocks are accompanied by images, including video and audio recordings.

Remember to use the hidden menus. Roll over the left edge of the screen to open the menu. Click to go directly to the topic of your choice.

★ VIRTUAL BUILDINGS

As you travel around the Time Capsule, you'll come to a window with a house in the distance. This is the Virtual Buildings station. Along the bottom of the window are four diamonds. As you roll the cursor over each diamond, the building in the window changes and the name of the building appears: Iroquois longhouse, log cabin, Victorian house, 1950s suburban home. Click the related diamond to travel to the building of your choice.

Walking Around the House   After clicking the picture, you'll find yourself outside the dwelling you have chosen. Each building is rendered with realistic and authentic detail. You can explore the building by navigating along a predetermined path. Click to the right to move right, to the left to move left, at the top of the screen to move forward, and at the bottom to move backward. Lost your bearings? Clicking the house icon at the bottom of the screen will bring up a floor plan showing the complete house, with the spot where you are standing highlighted in orange.

Within each building, a number of hot spots are available. You'll discover the hot spot when your cursor changes to a pointing finger as it rolls over an object. Click the object to learn more about it and related topics. For example, during your journey through the Iroquois longhouse, you will have the opportunity to see what foods are stored in the storage baskets, peer into the pot of stew that is cooking in the fire pit, hear Seneca social dance music, and learn about moccasins.

In each house, click the hot spots to
learn more about objects of interest.

★ INTERNET CONNECTION

If you have Internet access and a World Wide Web browser (such as Netscape, Mosaic, or the Web capability of one of the on-line services), you can use the CD-ROM to access the Prentice Hall homepage. To connect, quit the *American Heritage® History of the United States* program and open the Web folder on your CD-ROM. Then launch your web browser, open PRENHALL.HTML, and go to the Prentice Hall homepage to access the educational resources of the World Wide Web. For detailed instructions about connecting to the Internet, see the U.S. History Web Read Me file on the *American Heritage® History of the United States* CD-ROM.

Surfing the 'Net　After entering Prentice Hall's homepage, click the notebook to enter the site, then click "Social Studies". Here, you can find lesson strategies, student activities, and links to selected Internet sites that contain excellent resources for American history. These sites offer text, photos, and audio and video recordings.

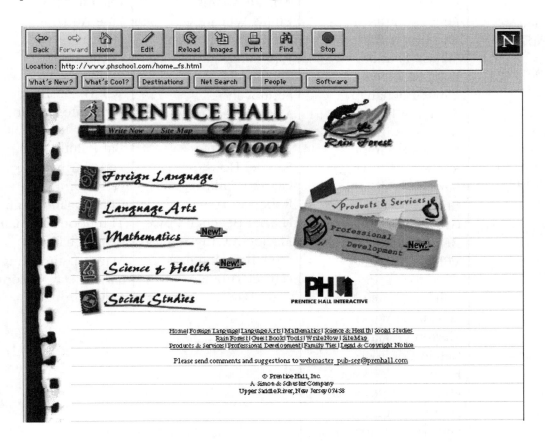

CD-ROM CONTENTS

TIME TOUR*	PRESIDENTS	HISTORY MAKERS	
A Meeting of Different Worlds	George Washington	Christopher Columbus	Hiram Revels
	John Adams	John Smith	Emily Dickinson
From Revolution to Republic	Thomas Jefferson	Pocahontas	Chief Joseph
	James Madison	William Penn	Andrew Carnegie
	James Monroe	Anne Hutchinson	Mark Twain
The New Republic	John Quincy Adams	Benjamin Franklin	Winslow Homer
	Andrew Jackson	Benjamin Banneker	Alfred T. Mahan
	Martin Van Buren	Daniel Boone	Thomas Edison
An Expanding Nation	William Henry Harrison	Patrick Henry	Samuel Gompers
	John Tyler	Abigail Adams	Ida Tarbell
	James K. Polk	Phillis Wheatley	Jane Addams
The Nation Torn Apart	Zachary Taylor	Alexander Hamilton	Henry Ford
	Millard Fillmore	John Marshall	Orville and
Reshaping the Nation	Franklin Pierce	Tecumseh	Wilbur Wright
	James Buchanan	Sequoyah	W.E.B. Du Bois
	Abraham Lincoln	Meriwether Lewis and William Clark	Jeannette Rankin
A New Role in the World	Andrew Johnson		Eleanor Roosevelt
	Ulysses S. Grant	Henry Clay	Babe Ruth
	Rutherford B. Hayes	Samuel Houston	Louis Armstrong
Prosperity, Depression, and War	James A. Garfield	George Catlin	Langston Hughes
	Chester A. Arthur	Robert E. Lee	Charles Lindbergh
	Grover Cleveland	Harriet Beecher Stowe	Thurgood Marshall
The Nation Today and Tomorrow	Benjamin Harrison	Elizabeth Cady Stanton	Cesar Chavez
	William McKinley	Frederick Douglass	Martin Luther King, Jr.
	Theodore Roosevelt	Harriet Tubman	Sandra Day O'Connor
	William Howard Taft	Clara Barton	Maya Lin
	Woodrow Wilson		
	Warren G. Harding		
	Calvin Coolidge		
	Herbert C. Hoover		
	Franklin D. Roosevelt		
	Harry S. Truman		
	Dwight D. Eisenhower		
	John F. Kennedy		
	Lyndon B. Johnson		
	Richard M. Nixon		
	Gerald R. Ford		
*For a detailed table of contents of the Time Tour, see page 90 of this Guidebook.	Jimmy Carter		
	Ronald W. Reagan		
	George H.W. Bush		
	William J. Clinton		

FACE THE ISSUES	LIBRARY	ARTS & ENTERTAINMENT	VIRTUAL BUILDINGS

The Great Compromise of the Constitutional Convention	Maps
	  U.S. Political
	  U.S. Physical
	  U.S. Satellite
		Music
		
		Books
		
		TV
			Iroquois Longhouse
			
			Log Cabin
			
			Victorian Home

Fugitive Slave Law	Documents
	  Declaration of
	  Independence
		Movies
		
		Sports
			1950s Suburban Home

Child Labor	Constitution
	  of the United
	  States		

Women's Suffrage	Report Maker Image Library		

Brown v. *Board of Education*	Bibliographies
	  Literature
	  History
	  Biography		

Vietnam War			

ABOUT THE CD-ROM EXPLORER

The *American Heritage® History of the United States* CD-ROM enriches the study of history for students. Developed as a companion to Prentice Hall's *The American Nation* program, the *History of the United States* CD-ROM can be used with *The American Nation* or any quality American history text.

The 31 CD-ROM Explorer activities on the pages that follow help students to use the *History of the United States* CD-ROM as an interactive research tool. Each activity focuses on an important topic in American history, from pre-history to the present. Students are offered opportunities for reading, writing, viewing, listening, manipulating materials, working independently or with others, and making presentations.

The CD-ROM Explorer activities guide students in accessing the CD-ROM to conduct research for specific assignments. The activity worksheets provide step-by-step instructions to locate information, take notes, and organize and prepare material for presentation. Students are guided to investigate all the sections of the CD-ROM, study the pictures, maps, and charts, and make use of the video and audio components that accompany the text. Some Explorer activities direct students to use the CD-ROM to log on to the Internet for additional research. Of course, students should be encouraged to refer to their textbooks and other print materials, as well.

In addition to using the worksheet write-on lines, students can take research notes for their projects in the CD-ROM's on-screen Notebook. This electronic notepad is available at all times when the CD-ROM is in use. A word processor called the Report Maker provides students with a presentation tool for their final product. Students can paste notes from the Notebook into the Report Maker. They can also attach pictures from the CD-ROM Image Library to enhance their reports.

CD-ROM Explorer

ACTIVITY 1
American Rivers

This activity will help you learn about American rivers. Follow these instructions to write an outline for a TV documentary about one or more rivers in North America. The CD-ROM *American Heritage® History of the United States* will help you research the topic. Use this guide to track your exploration.

1. In the Time Capsule, go to the Library. Click the wall map to access the physical map of the United States. On the map, locate five major North American rivers. Write the names of the rivers on the lines below. Then, use the on-screen Notebook to make notes about the location and other geographical facts about each river.

    _____

    _____

    _____

2. Decide how to focus your documentary. Which river(s) will you cover? What will be the theme of the documentary? From what point of view will you present the narrative? Write your responses to these questions on the lines below.

    _____

    _____

3. Now that you have focused your topic, research your documentary using the Internet. Quit the *American Heritage® History of the United States* program. Launch your web browser and type http://www.yahoo.com in the location field. Use Yahoo to find a list of search engines. Use different engines to search for information about your topic.
    Keep track of your search on the lines that follow by listing keywords and addresses that resulted in helpful information. Add new facts to the on-screen Notebook.

    Key Words: _____

    _____

    _____

Addresses: _____

_____

_____

_____

4. Decide the three to five main points your documentary will make. Write these points on the lines below.

_____

_____

_____

_____

_____

_____

_____

_____

5. In the Report Maker, write the outline for your documentary. Use information from your Notebook file. Be sure to include notes about the visual and audio aspects of your film. If you present your outline in the Report Maker, you can include pictures from the Image Library. If you print it out, list the pictures that go with your outline.

 **CD-ROM Explorer**

ACTIVITY 2
The Incas

You have just taken a job with the Time Travel Tourist Agency. Your first assignment is to create a brochure that makes people want to go back in time to visit the Incas. Use the CD-ROM *American Heritage® History of the United States* and the internet to research the topic. Follow the guide below to prepare your brochure.

1. Use the CD-ROM Index to search for references to the Incas. Click the Index reference to access the discussion of the Incas in the Time Tour. Then click the map icon to see the map "Great Civilizations of the Americas." Locate the Inca civilization on the map. Describe this location on the lines below. Use the on-screen Notebook to make notes on what you have learned.

_____

_____

2. Your next stop will be the Internet. Quit the *American Heritage® History of the United States* program. Then launch your web browser.

   In the location field, type http://www.yahoo.com. Use Yahoo to find a list of search engines. Use different engines to search for information about the Incas. Some key words to use in your search are *Macchu Picchu, Andes, Cuzco,* and *Quechua.*

   Keep track of your search on the lines that follow by listing key words and addresses that resulted in helpful information. Add new facts to the on-screen Notebook.

   Key Words: _____

   _____

   _____

   Addresses:_____

   _____

   _____

   _____

3. Decide on the kind of tour the brochure will promote. What places in the Inca empire will tourists visit? What people or events will they see? What foods will they eat? What recreation will be available? Make notes on the lines below.

Places: _____

_____

People or events: _____

_____

Foods: _____

_____

Recreation: _____

_____

4. You are now ready to decide on the organization and layout of your brochure. Use the space below to describe how you will set up your brochure. Be sure to include ideas for illustrations.

_____

_____

_____

_____

5. Compile your notes and the information you have gathered. Write and design your Time Travel brochure on the Incas. Share it with the class.

CD-ROM Explorer

ACTIVITY 3
Trade in New France

In this activity, you will use information that you research and compile to write a story about a fur trader in New France. The CD-ROM *American Heritage® History of the United States* will help you research the topic and plan your story. Use this guide to track your exploration.

1. Search the CD-ROM Index to find the references to French colonists in North America. Access this reference and take notes in the on-screen Notebook.

2. Now, read the passage below. As you read, list historical characters you might use in your story on the lines below.

> Most French colonists were fur trappers and traders. Because they lived in the woods, they became known as *coureurs de bois*, or runners of the woods. Coureurs de bois learned from Native Americans how to trap and survive in the woods. Many married Indian women. Indians taught the French how to build and use canoes.
>
> Each fall, Indians and trappers paddled up the St. Lawrence to winter trapping grounds. There they trapped beaver, otter, mink, and other fur-bearing animals. In the spring, trappers loaded the furs they collected into canoes for the trip back down the St. Lawrence. They sold the furs to merchants on ships bound for France, where they sold for high prices.
>
> Many European merchants wanted a share of these high profits. This led to fierce competition for control of the fur trade. The French traded with the Algonquins and became their allies. The Algonquins were long-time enemies of the Iroquois. When the Dutch began to trade for furs with the Iroquois, the French and the Algonquins tried to block them. For many years, fighting raged among Europeans and their Indian allies.

_____

_____

_____

_____

_____

3. Visit the Iroquois longhouse in the Virtual Buildings section of the CD-ROM. Record ideas this visit gives you for your story setting in the on-screen Notebook.

4. Now you are ready to write your story. Compile the notes and other information that you have gathered. In the space below, list the main story elements you will use.

Characters: _____

_____

_____

Setting: _____

_____

_____

Plot: _____

_____

_____

Historical Details: _____

_____

_____

5. Use the Report Maker to write your story. After revising and editing your story, you may wish to share it with the class.

CD-ROM Explorer

ACTIVITY 4
The English Colonies

In this activity, you will create an interactive question and answer game based on information about the English colonies. The CD-ROM *American Heritage® History of the United States* will help you research the game. Use this guide to track your exploration.

1. Enter the Time Capsule and click the Time Tour. Locate and read the section "The First English Colonies." (For help in locating the section, consult the detailed Time Tour contents on page 90 of this Guidebook.) Take notes on what you read in the on-screen Notebook. Be sure to include where you found each fact when you take notes.

2. Look at the maps that show the English colonies. List the colonies in the chart below. Take notes in the on-screen Notebook on the location and geography of the colonies.

New England	Middle	Southern
_____	_____	_____
_____	_____	_____
_____	_____	_____
_____	_____	_____
_____	_____	_____

3. You will find information about people who lived in the English colonies in History Makers. Use the Index to search people such as Pocahontas, John Smith, Anne Hutchinson, William Penn, Benjamin Franklin, and Phillis Wheatley. Choose three people and read their biographies carefully. List the biographies you read on the lines below. Take notes in the on-screen Notebook.

_____

_____

4. Explore the Arts and Entertainment section of the CD-ROM to learn about the cultural life of people in the English colonies. Take notes on colonial literature and music in the on-screen Notebook.

5. Use your notes to write 20 questions about the English colonies that can be answered from the CD-ROM. Keep a record of where each answer can be found. To get started, write three sample questions and answers on the lines below. Then create the remaining questions in the Report Maker. You might consider including a question or two based on the pictures in the Image Library that you can access from the Report Maker.

Question 1: _____

_____

Answer 1: _____

_____

Question 2: _____

_____

Answer 2: _____

_____

Question 3: _____

_____

Answer 3: _____

_____

6. Challenge classmates to use the CD-ROM to find the answers to your questions.

Name _____ Class _____ Date _____

 CD-ROM Explorer

ACTIVITY 5
British Policies in the American Colonies

Suppose you could interview an American colonist in the 1760s. What questions would you ask? The CD-ROM *American Heritage® History of the United States* will help you research the years leading up to the Revolutionary War and compose an imaginary interview. Use this guide to track your exploration.

1. Access the Time Tour and read the chapter "The Road to Revolution." (For help in locating the chapter, consult the detailed Time Tour Contents on page 90 of this Guidebook.) Click the blue hot spots to listen to the accompanying audio. Take notes in the on-screen Notebook.

2. In the chapter, click the red hot spots for references to related topics. List the references on the lines below. Then explore each reference and make notes in the on-screen Notebook.

   _____

   _____

   _____

3. Now think about the questions you will ask the colonist. Brainstorm for a list of possible issues related to Britain's policies in the American colonies. List the issues on the lines below. When you are finished brainstorming, choose three key issues you will discuss. List them below.

   Possible Issues: _____

   _____

   _____

   Issues to discuss: _____

   _____

   _____

4. Brainstorm for a list of interview questions. Record the questions in the on-screen Notebook.

5. Who will you interview? Will you talk to a patriot or a loyalist? What point of view will that person have about the issues you listed above? Fill in the chart below to summarize the point of view for each issue.

Issue   Point of View

_____   _____

                                         _____

_____   _____

                                         _____

_____   _____

                                         _____

6. Compile your notes. Then use the Report Maker to write the questions and answers for your imaginary interview. You may wish to include pictures from the Image Library in your final presentation.

7. Present the interview to a small group of students. Take on the role of the interviewer and ask a classmate to play the colonist.

CD-ROM Explorer

ACTIVITY 6
The Continental Army

In this activity, you will prepare an illustrated article for a history magazine about the Continental Army. The CD-ROM *American Heritage® History of the United States* will help you research the topic. Use this guide to track your exploration.

1. Search the CD-ROM Index in the right scroll-out menu to locate references to the Continental Army. List the references on the lines below. (Hint: You should find references in the Time Tour, Presidents, and History Makers sections.)

_____

_____

_____

2. Explore the references in the Time Tour. As you scroll through the text, be sure to access the maps that show the battles between the Continental Army and the British. Also click on the blue hot spots to listen to the accompanying audio. Take notes on what you read and hear in the on-screen Notebook.

3. Explore the Continental Army reference in the Presidents section. Make notes in the on-screen Notebook.

4. Explore the Continental Army reference in the History Makers section. Take research notes in the on-screen Notebook.

5. Compile your notes on the Continental Army. Then decide on a focus for your article. Will you concentrate on the battles the Continental Army fought? The hardships endured by the soldiers? The daily life of a common soldier? The officers who led the troops? Write a sentence describing the focus of your article below.

_____

_____

_____

6. Go to the Library and click the Report Maker. Then access the Image Library to find images related to the American Revolution. Select images to illustrate your article. List the images on the lines below.

_____

_____

_____

7. Draft your article in the Report Maker. Use information from your Notebook file. Remember to start your article with a strong topic sentence.

8. Ask a partner to read your article and suggest improvements. Then revise and polish the article. Illustrate the article by attaching the images you selected from the Image Library.

 **CD-ROM Explorer**

ACTIVITY 7
The Constitutional Convention

What was the Constitutional Convention like? In this activity, you will have a chance to imagine that historic meeting. Your assignment is to write a script for a discussion that might have taken place at the Constitutional Convention. The CD-ROM *American Heritage® History of the United States* will help you research the topic. Use this guide to track your exploration.

1. Search the Index in the right scroll-out menu to find references to the Articles of Confederation and the Constitutional Convention. List the references on the lines below.

   _____

   _____

   _____

2. Explore the references in the Time Tour. Take notes in the on-screen Notebook.

3. Go to History Makers and access the following biographies: Benjamin Franklin, Patrick Henry, and Alexander Hamilton. Next, go to the Presidents section and access the biography of James Madison. As you read and listen, take notes in the on-screen Notebook. Then write at least one statement each person might have made about the Constitution on the lines below.

   Benjamin Franklin: _____

   _____

   Patrick Henry: _____

   _____

   Alexander Hamilton: _____

   _____

   James Madison: _____

   _____

4. Now, in the left scroll-out menu, access Face the Issues. Click "The Great Compromise of the Constitutional Convention." Explore each screen. Listen to each speaker. Make notes about what you read and hear in the on-screen Notebook.

5. Decide on the characters you will use in your script and the issues they will discuss. Record your decisions on the lines below.

Characters: _____

_____

_____

Issues: _____

_____

_____

6. Compile the notes you have taken. Then access the Report Maker and write a draft of your script.

7. Work with a partner or small group to revise and polish your script. When your script is complete, invite classmates to help you read it aloud.

 **CD-ROM Explorer**

ACTIVITY 8
Election of 1800

Today, political parties can use the Internet to communicate with the American public. Many parties have a homepage on the World Wide Web. In this activity, you will learn about the election of 1800. Then you will create the text and pictures for a homepage for one of the two parties that campaigned during this election. The CD-ROM *American Heritage® History of the United States* will help you research the party you choose. Use this guide to track your exploration.

1. In the Index in the right scroll-out menu, search the following topics: election of 1800, Democratic Republican party, Federalist party, Aaron Burr. List the references you find on the lines below.

   _____

   _____

2. Explore the references in the Time Tour. Take notes in the Notebook.

3. From the left scroll-out menu, access the Presidents section. Then go to the biography of Thomas Jefferson, and read about the election of 1800. Take notes in the on-screen Notebook.

4. Alexander Hamilton was an important Federalist. Access History Makers to locate information on Hamilton. Read about his role in the Federalist party, and take notes in the on-screen Notebook.

5. Decide which party—Federalists or Democratic Republicans—you want to represent. Write the name of the party and some key information about it on the lines below.

   Political Party: _____

   Key Information: _____

   _____

   _____

   _____

6. Now decide what the main message of your party's homepage will be. Write your ideas on the lines below.

    _____

    _____

    _____

    _____

7. Go to the Report Maker and access the Image Library. Review related images, such as those of Thomas Jefferson, Alexander Hamilton, and the White House. List the picture(s) that you will include on your homepage below.

    _____

    _____

    _____

8. Review your notes in the on-screen Notebook. Write the text for your party's homepage in the Report Maker. Attach the images that you listed above. If you plan to include other graphic elements, describe them next to the text where they will appear.

★ ★ ★ ★ ★ ★ ★ ★ ★ ★ ★ ★ ★ ★ ★ ★

 # CD-ROM Explorer

ACTIVITY 9
Lewis and Clark

In this activity, you will write a script for a scene of a movie based on the experiences of Meriwether Lewis and William Clark. The CD-ROM *American Heritage® History of the United States* will help you research the topic. Use this guide to track your exploration.

1. Access the Index and search the following topics: Lewis and Clark, Louisiana Purchase, Sacajawea. List the references you find below.

    _____

    _____

2. In the Time Tour, access the reference to the explorations of Lewis and Clark. Read the text carefully. Then click the map icons to access the maps "The Louisiana Purchase" and "Lewis and Clark Cross the Continental Divide." Based on the maps, on the lines below list rivers, mountains, and other geographic features that the explorers would have seen on their journey.

    _____

    _____

3. Access History Makers from the left scroll-out menu. Then read the biography of Lewis and Clark. Take notes in the on-screen Notebook.

4. Decide on the focus of your movie scene. What characters will appear in it? Where will it be set? What events will take place? Write your decisions on the lines below.

    Characters: _____

    _____

    Setting: _____

    _____

    Events: _____

    _____

5. Using the information that you have gathered, write the script for your Lewis and Clark movie scene in the Report Maker.

6. Now create a storyboard showing the main plot and visual elements of your scene. Draw a first draft of your storyboard in the grid below. Revise this draft and attach a final version to your script.

CD-ROM Explorer

ACTIVITY 10
The Industrial Revolution

In this activity, you will create a mural about the early stages of the Industrial Revolution in the United States. Use the CD-ROM *American Heritage® History of the United States* to help you research the topic. Use this guide to track your exploration.

1. Access the CD-ROM Index in the right scroll-out menu. Search the Index for references to the Industrial Revolution. In addition, look up the following key words: inventions, steamboats, John Deere, Cyrus McCormick, and Samuel F.B. Morse. List the references that you find on the lines below.

    _____

    _____

    _____

    _____

2. Explore the references you listed above. Click the blue hot spot to access the audio about the mill town of Lowell, Massachusetts. Click the red hot spots to access other references about factory life. Take notes in the on-screen Notebook. Be sure to record where you found each piece of information.

3. Transportation improved during the 1800s. Canals were built to help western farmers get their products to markets in the East. In the Time Tour, access the chapter "Years of Growth and Expansion" to read about the creation of canals in the 1800s. Study the map "Major Canals." List at least three canals on the lines below. Make notes in the on-screen Notebook.

    _____

    _____

    _____

    _____

4. Review the notes that you made in the on-screen Notebook. Then brainstorm for a list of topics you might depict in your mural. List the topics on the lines below.

_____

_____

_____

_____

5. Create your mural. Draw a first sketch in the box below.

6. In the Report Maker, write a paragraph describing your mural and what you are trying to convey about the Industrial Revolution.

CD-ROM Explorer

ACTIVITY 11
The Age of Andrew Jackson

Imagine that you could sit in on a conversation between President Andrew Jackson and the Cherokee leader Sequoyah. What might they say to one another? How would they behave? The CD-ROM *American Heritage® History of the United States* will help you research President Jackson and Sequoyah and the important events of their time. You will use this research to write a conversation that might have taken place between Jackson and Sequoyah. Use this guide to track your exploration.

1. In the Time Capsule, go to the Presidents section and click Andrew Jackson. As you read and listen to the material about Jackson, pay special attention to information that might help you imagine what he would say to Sequoyah. Use the on-screen Notebook to record at least two useful pieces of information.

2. Now that you know Andrew Jackson a little bit, what do you think he might say to a Native American leader? List your ideas below.

   _____

   _____

   _____

   _____

   _____

3. Access History Makers to learn more about Sequoyah. Read the biography of Sequoyah and make notes in the on-screen Notebook. What topics might Sequoyah discuss in a conversation with Jackson? Write your ideas on the lines below.

   _____

   _____

   _____

   _____

   _____

4. Go to the right scroll-out menu and use the Index to find other information about Jackson. Look up the following key words: Cherokee, Indian Removal Act, and Trail of Tears. Add notes to the on-screen Notebook.

5. Now you are ready to prepare the conversation between Jackson and Sequoyah. In the space below, list the topics they would discuss. Next to each topic, jot down a few words reflecting each man's opinions about it.

Topic	Jackson	Sequoyah
_____	_____	_____
	_____	_____
_____	_____	_____
	_____	_____
_____	_____	_____
	_____	_____
_____	_____	_____
	_____	_____

6. How might each man behave during the conversation? Use the space below to describe each man's attitude toward the other. Give reasons to support your ideas.

Jackson: _____

_____

_____

Sequoyah: _____

_____

_____

7. Use the on-screen Report Maker to write the conversation between Jackson and Sequoyah. Keep in mind the ideas each man would express as well as the attitudes each would convey. When you are satisfied with the conversation you have written, practice acting it out with a partner. If you want to wear costumes or make scenery, look through the pictures on the CD-ROM for ideas.

 # CD-ROM Explorer

ACTIVITY 12
On the Oregon Trail

What was life like on the Oregon Trail? In this activity, you will imagine you are a pioneer traveling west on the Trail. You will write a letter to a friend back east describing your experiences. The CD-ROM *American Heritage® History of the United States* will help you get started. Use this guide to track your exploration.

1. In the Time Capsule, go to the Time Tour. Then click the chapter "From Sea to Shining Sea," and read about the settlement of Oregon. For help in locating the chapters, consult the detailed Time Tour contents on page 90 of this Guidebook. Take notes in the on-screen Notebook.

2. While in the Time Tour, study the map "Oregon Country." Next, locate the map "Trails to the West" near the end of the chapter under "A Nation's Dream Comes True." Based on the maps, on the lines below list at least two rivers and a major landform that the Oregon Trail crossed.

    Rivers: _____

    _____

    Landform: _____

3. Study the maps mentioned above more closely to learn more about the Oregon Trail and the land it traveled through. For example, you might find out where the Oregon Trail began, the length of the trail, other trails that crossed it or split off from it, and communities or landmarks that were located along the way. This information will be useful in describing the setting of the trail in your letter. Record your findings in the on-screen Notebook.

4. In the left pull-out menu, click the chapter "The First Americans" in the Time Tour. In the chapter, find the map "Native American Culture Areas." On the lines below, list the Native American groups that travelers on the Oregon Trail might have encountered. Use the material in the chapter to record one fact about each group's way of life.

    _____

    _____

5. Go to the History Makers section and locate the biography of George Catlin. Read about his travels and trace them on the "Trails to the West" map. What do you think Catlin might have said to pioneers about Native Americans? Write your ideas on the lines below.

_____

_____

_____

6. Go to the Internet by quitting the program. Then launch your web browser. In the location field, type http://www.yahoo.com. Use Yahoo to find a list of search engines. Using different engines search for information about the Oregon Trail. On the lines below, list addresses that resulted in helpful information. Add new facts to the on-screen Notebook.

Addresses: _____

_____

_____

_____

_____

7. Before drafting your letter, listen to pioneer music to help get you in the mood. Return to the Time Capsule and access the Arts and Entertainment section. Search for "Songs of the Frontier." Write the names of the songs that you find below.

_____

_____

8. In the Report Maker, write your letter. Include pictures from the Image Library to show your friend back home what the Oregon Trail and the West were like.

 CD-ROM Explorer

ACTIVITY 13
The Cotton Kingdom

In this activity, you will plan a dramatic presentation about life in the South before 1861. Use the CD-ROM *American Heritage® History of the United States* to help you research the topic. Use this guide to track your exploration.

1. Go to the Time Tour. In the unit "An Expanding Nation," click the chapter "The Worlds of North and South." Explore the section "Life in the Cotton Kingdom." Make notes in the on-screen Notebook.

2. While you are in the Time Tour, locate the map "Products of the South." On the lines below, list at least three main products of the southern states in the mid-1800s.

_____

_____

_____

3. Next, go to the History Makers section. Read the biographies of Harriet Beecher Stowe, Harriet Tubman, and Frederick Douglass. Take notes in the on-screen Notebook. Then, on the lines below, write a statement that each of these history makers might have made about life in the Cotton Kingdom.

Harriet Beecher Stowe: _____

_____

_____

Harriet Tubman: _____

_____

_____

Frederick Douglass: _____

_____

_____

4. Go to Arts and Entertainment and explore the sections on Music and Books. On the lines below, record two kinds of African American music performed in the 1800s. List the title of a book about enslaved African Americans written at the time.

Music: _____

_____

Book: _____

5. Access the Report Maker, and scroll through the Image Library. Find and attach pictures that portray life in the South before the Civil War.

6. Now you are ready to decide what kind of dramatic presentation you will create. Will it include music? Will you narrate it while others act it out? Will you present images with narration? Write your ideas below.

_____

_____

_____

_____

_____

7. In the Report Maker, write a dramatic presentation about life in the Cotton Kingdom before 1861. Base your presentation on the material you have gathered. When your presentation is complete, you might share it with the class.

 **CD-ROM Explorer**

ACTIVITY 14
The Underground Railroad

In this activity, you will write the script of a conversation that you might have had with someone from the mid-1800s about the underground railroad. The CD-ROM *American Heritage® History of the United States* will help you research the topic. Use this guide to track your exploration.

1. From the Time Capsule, access the Time Tour. In the unit "An Expanding Nation," click the chapter "A Reforming Age" and read the section "Liberty for All." Then skim through the section "Women Are Created Equal." Click the blue hot spot to hear Sojourner Truth's famous speech about the role of women. Make notes in the Notebook.

2. Access History Makers and explore the biographies of Harriet Tubman and Frederick Douglass. Be sure to click the blue hot spots to hear the audio recordings that accompany the biographies. When you have finished reading and listening, write a sample question that you might ask each of these History Makers about the underground railroad. Make additional notes about Tubman and Douglass in the on-screen Notebook.

   Harriet Tubman:_____

   _____

   Frederick Douglass: _____

   _____

3. While you are in the History Makers section, find and read the biography of Harriet Beecher Stowe. Be sure to listen to the excerpt from her book *Uncle Tom's Cabin*. On the lines below, write words to describe the feelings and problems that an escaping slave might have.

   <u>Feelings</u>   <u>Problems</u>

   _____   _____

   _____   _____

   _____   _____

   _____   _____

   _____   _____

4. Now go to Arts and Entertainment and explore the Music section. On the lines below, write the names of two the spirituals that African Americans used to help them in their escape from slavery. Explain how they were used. Then write the names of two spirituals that you might research further. Add notes about the use of spirituals in the on-screen Notebook.

Spirituals used in escape: _____

_____

Spirituals to research: _____

_____

5. Reread the notes that you have made for this assignment. Brainstorm for a list of people you might talk to about the underground railroad. Jot down what the focus of the conversation with each person might be. When you are finished brainstorming, choose the person you will use for the conversation. Put a check next to the name in the list below.

Person	Focus of Conversation
_____	_____
_____	_____
_____	_____

6. Cut and paste your notes from the Notebook into the Report Maker. Use these notes to help you write a script of an imaginary conversation with someone from the mid-1800s about the underground railroad. With a partner, act out the conversation for the class.

 **CD-ROM Explorer**

ACTIVITY 15
Slavery in the Western Territories

As new territories applied for statehood in the mid- to late 1800s, the issue of slavery heated up and threatened to tear the nation apart. In this activity, you will research how the slavery issue affected the administrations of four American Presidents. Then you will write a description of the role that the issue of slavery played during each President's administration. The CD-ROM *American Heritage® History of the United States* will help you research the topic. Use this guide to track your exploration.

1. In the Time Tour, find and explore the chapter "The Road to Civil War." Pay special attention to the subsections "A Compromise at Last," "Kansas-Nebraska Act," and "The Dred Scott Decision." As you read, take notes in the on-screen Notebook.

2. Now go to Face the Issues. Access the issue "The Fugitive Slave Law." Read through this section carefully. On the lines below, record the names of at least four key people and their positions on the Fugitive Slave Law. Make additional notes in the on-screen Notebook.

Key People   Position

_____   _____

                                                _____

_____   _____

                                                _____

_____   _____

                                                _____

_____   _____

                                                _____

3. Go to History Makers and skim through the biographies of Henry Clay and Frederick Douglass. Add notes on their contribution to the debate about slavery to the on-screen Notebook.

4. In the Presidents section, access the following: Zachary Taylor, Millard Fillmore, Franklin Pierce, and James Buchanan. On the lines below, list the Presidents' names. Next to each President, write the legislation or major events related to slavery during his administration. Then record each President's position on the legislation or events. Take additional notes in the on-screen Notebook.

President	Legislation or Event	President's Position
_____	_____	_____
	_____	_____
_____	_____	_____
	_____	_____
_____	_____	_____
	_____	_____
_____	_____	_____
	_____	_____

5. In the Report Maker, draft four paragraphs, one for each of the Presidents you researched. Explain the role that the issue of slavery played during each President's administration. If you wish, find pictures of the Presidents in the Image Library and attach them to your report.

★ ★ ★ ★ ★ ★ ★ ★ ★ ★ ★ ★ ★ ★ ★ ★

 # CD-ROM Explorer

ACTIVITY 16
The Blue and the Gray

In this activity, you will create a memorial about the Civil War. You will also write a dedication speech for the memorial. The CD-ROM *American Heritage® History of the United States* will help you research the topic. Use this guide to track your exploration.

1. Use the left scroll-out menu to access "Torn by War," located in the unit "The Nation Torn Apart" in the Time Tour. As you read the chapter, click the blue hot spots to listen to the words of Abraham Lincoln. Take notes in the on-screen Notebook.

2. While you are exploring "Torn by War," study the map "The Final Battles." List two Union victories and two Confederate victories below.

_____

_____

_____

3. Go to History Makers and access the biographies of Robert E. Lee and Clara Barton. As you read, take notes in the on-screen Notebook.

4. Go to the Presidents section and access the biography of Abraham Lincoln. Add notes on Lincoln to the on-screen Notebook.

5. Use the left scroll-out menu to access Arts and Entertainment. Find all references to the Civil War. Add to your notes in the Notebook.

6. Based on your exploration, decide on the memorial you will create. What form will the memorial take—a plaque, a statue, a fountain, a work of art? Who or what will the memorial commemorate? Will it commemorate Union soldiers, Confederate soldiers, African American soldiers, nurses, a political leader? Will it commemorate a particular battle? Will it commemorate the ending of the war?

Form of Memorial: _____

Person(s) or Event Commemorated: _____

7. Now create your memorial. Draw a picture, build a model, or describe the memorial in words. You can use the space below to sketch out your ideas.

8. In the Report Maker, write the dedication speech for your memorial, using the notes you have made in the on-screen Notebook. Conduct a dedication ceremony for a small group of classmates.

 **CD-ROM Explorer**

ACTIVITY 17
Reconstruction

In this activity, you will create a test on Reconstruction. The CD-ROM *American Heritage® History of the United States* will help you research what happened after the Civil War. Use this guide to track your exploration.

1. In the Time Capsule, access the Time Tour. Click the chapter "Rebuilding the Nation" in the unit "The Nation Torn Apart." Pay special attention to the section "Help for Freemen." Click the blue hot spots for audio on the freedmen. As you read and listen, record facts for your test in the on-screen Notebook. Remember, you will have to provide answers for any questions that you ask. Be sure to include the source of each fact in your notes.

2. Next, go to the Presidents section. Identify the three Presidents who held office after Abraham Lincoln was assassinated. List these Reconstruction Presidents on the lines below. Take notes about these Presidents in the on-screen Notebook.

   _____

   _____

   _____

3. Access the History Makers section and click "Hiram Revels." Read the biography of Revels and make notes in the on-screen Notebook.

4. In the Report Maker, access the Image Library. Search for pictures related to the Reconstruction period. For example, you can find a picture of each Reconstruction President in the Image Library. List pictures that you find on the lines below. Add notes about the pictures to the on-screen Notebook.

   _____

   _____

   _____

   _____

   _____

5. Decide on the kind of test questions you will write. Will they be multiple-choice questions? Matching questions? Fill-in-the-blanks? Or will you use a combination of question types? Be sure to include at least one essay question. And you might base a question on a picture you selected from the Image Library. On the lines below, identify the kind of test questions you will use and then write two sample questions and answers.

Kind of Test Questions: _____

_____

Question 1: _____

_____

Answer 1: _____

_____

Question 2: _____

_____

Answer 2: _____

_____

6. In the Report Maker, create a test made up of 10 questions about Reconstruction based on your research notes. Try to focus your questions on important issues. Then write answers to the questions. Print out the test and have several classmates complete it. Tell them they can use the CD-ROM to research their answers. Check their answers when they are done.

 **CD-ROM Explorer**

ACTIVITY 18
On the Plains

Imagine that you are a pioneer who has settled on the Great Plains. You and your family are starting a farm. In this activity, you will write a diary entry about your life on the Plains. The CD-ROM *American Heritage® History of the United States* will help you research background information about life on a Great Plains farm. Use this guide to track your exploration.

1. In the Time Tour, access the chapter "The Frontier West." Scroll through the chapter until you reach the subsection "Farming on the Plains." Read from here to the end of the chapter. Be sure to access the audio selection in which Elinore Pruitt Stewart describes her life on a Plains farm. Take notes in the on-screen Notebook as you listen and read. On the lines below, list any references indicated by red hot spots that you might wish to explore later.

   _____

   _____

2. While in the chapter "The Frontier West," find and access the map "Opening the West." Use the map to decide where on the Great Plains to locate your farm. (If you need help in identifying the Great Plains, refer to the physical map in the Library.) Record the location of your farm below.

   Location: _____

   _____

3. Select the pioneer whose diary entry you will write. Will you be the farmer? His wife? One of the children? List the character you choose and at least two activities that this character might include in a diary entry on the lines below.

   Character: _____

   Activities:_____

   _____

   _____

4. There were few trees on the Great Plains, and most Plains farmers had to content themselves with shelters made of sod. The way of life in these rough huts was similar, however, to that of pioneers who built log cabins on the earlier frontier. On the left scroll-out menu, roll over "Virtual Buildings" and click "Log Cabin" on the submenu that appears. As you tour the log cabin, list facts about pioneer cooking, furnishings, and daily chores on the lines below. Pay special attention to the activities you listed for question 3. Record more detailed notes in the on-screen Notebook.

Cooking: _____

_____

Furnishings: _____

_____

Chores: _____

_____

5. Although farm life was hard on the Great Plains, people had fun, too. Go to Arts and Entertainment to learn about the kind of music people on the frontier enjoyed. Write the names of two songs on the lines below.

_____

_____

6. Your diary entry will be more vivid if you include pictures. Explore the Image Library in the Report Maker to find pictures that you could use to illustrate your diary entry. List the pictures on the lines below.

_____

_____

7. Write your diary entry in the Report Maker. Base it on the research notes that you took. Attach the pictures that you selected in the Image Library. When your entry is complete, share it with the class.

CD-ROM Explorer

ACTIVITY 19
Business and Industry

Between 1865 and 1914, the rapid growth of business and industry made the United States rich. But it also created problems. In this activity, you will find out about early American industrial growth. You will also learn about the accompanying problem of child labor. Then you will write an editorial supporting or opposing child labor laws, using the voice of a History Maker of the time. The CD-ROM *American Heritage® History of the United States* will help you research the topic. Use this guide to track your exploration.

1. Go to the Time Tour, and skim the chapter "The Rise of Industry." Pay special attention to the subsection "A New Kind of Workplace." Click the blue hot spots to hear the audio selections featuring Congressman John Reagan's attack on monopoly and inventor's assistant Thomas Watson's description of the invention of the telephone. View the video footage of early automobile factories and the Model T. Take research notes in the on-screen Notebook.

2. Access History Makers and read the following biographies: Andrew Carnegie, Samuel Gompers, Henry Ford, Ida Tarbell, and Thomas Edison. On the lines below, briefly explain how each person contributed to or reacted to the growth of business and industry. Make more detailed notes in the on-screen Notebook.

Andrew Carnegie: _____

_____

Samuel Gompers: _____

_____

Henry Ford: _____

_____

Ida Tarbell: _____

_____

Thomas Edison: _____

_____

3. Access Face the Issues and explore "Child Labor Laws." Take notes on what you read and hear in the on-screen Notebook. On the lines below, list at least one argument in favor of child labor and one argument against it.

For: _____

_____

Against: _____

_____

4. Review the notes you have taken. Then, on the lines below, identify the History Maker whose opinions you will present in your editorial about child labor laws. Jot down a few key words summarizing that person's point of view on the topic.

History Maker: _____

Point of View: _____

_____

5. Writing as if you were the History Maker identified in Question 4, draft your editorial in the Report Maker. Begin by stating the issue and your position on it. Then use details and examples from your notes to write several paragraphs supporting your position.

6. Review your first draft, make revisions, and then prepare a final version. Scroll through the Image Library to see if there are any pictures that you might attach to the editorial.

CD-ROM Explorer

ACTIVITY 20
In the City

In this activity, you will create an illustrated chart about American city life in the late 1800s and early 1900s. The chart will compare the lives of two kinds of city-dwellers: the poor and the middle class. The CD-ROM *American Heritage® History of the United States* will help you research information. Use this guide to track your exploration.

1. In the on-screen Notebook, write the following headings: The Poor, The Middle Class, Both. Use these headings to organize the notes that you take as you explore the CD-ROM.

2. Use the left scroll-out menu to access the chapter "A Diverse Nation" in the Time Tour unit "Reshaping the Nation." As you scroll through the chapter, click the blue hot spots to hear immigrants Rosa Cristoforo and Pardee Lowe describe their experiences. Also be sure to access the video footage showing immigrants in their new land. On the lines below, list any references you wish to follow up.

   _____

   _____

3. Access History Makers and click "Jane Addams." As you read Addams' biography, click the blue hot spot to hear the audio selection. On the lines below, summarize Addams' contribution to city life. Take additional notes in the on-screen Notebook.

   _____

   _____

   _____

   _____

   _____

4. For vivid information about the children of the poor, access Face the Issues and click "Child Labor Laws." Take notes in the on-screen Notebook about what you read, see, and hear in this section.

5. In the left scroll-out menu, roll over Virtual Buildings and then click "Victorian House" in the submenu that appears. Explore this building to see how the middle class lived in the late 1800s. On the lines below, list some details about this way of life. Take additional notes in the on-screen Notebook.

Furnishings: _____

_____

Customs: _____

_____

Pastimes: _____

_____

6. To learn about popular culture in the nation's cities in the late 1800s and early 1900s, explore Arts and Entertainment. On the lines below, list music, literature, and sports available at this time. Add notes to the on-screen Notebook.

Music: _____

_____

Literature: _____

_____

Sports: _____

_____

7. Review your notes. Then create a chart comparing the experiences of city life for the poor and the middle class in the late 1800s and early 1900s. Show how life was similar and different for these two groups. Illustrate your chart by attaching pictures from the Image Bank. After revising and editing your work, display your chart for the class.

★ ★ ★ ★ ★ ★ ★ ★ ★ ★ ★ ★ ★ ★ ★

 # CD-ROM Explorer

ACTIVITY 21
The Suffragists

Imagine that you are a tour guide. Instead of taking people on tours through places, however, you take them on tours through history. In this assignment, you will write a description of a historical tour of the suffragist movement. The CD-ROM *American Heritage® History of the United States* will help you research the suffragist movement. Use this guide to track your exploration.

1. In the Time Capsule, access Face the Issues. Locate and read the section "Women's Suffrage." On the lines below, list at least three people or groups mentioned in the section. Note the position of each on giving women the vote. Take additional research notes on the suffrage movement in the on-screen Notebook. Remember to include interesting anecdotes that you can use to enliven your history tour.

<u>Person or Group</u>   <u>Position</u>

_____   _____

_____   _____

_____   _____

_____   _____

_____   _____

2. Use the right scroll-out menu to access the Index. Search the Index for references to women's suffrage and suffragists. List any references that you find on the lines below.

_____

_____

_____

_____

3. Explore the references in the Time Tour that you listed above. Watch for the video footage showing suffragists. Take notes in the on-screen Notebook about what you have read and seen.

4. Next, pull up the left scroll-out menu and click "History Makers." Once you are in History Makers, find and read the following biographies: Elizabeth Cady Stanton, Jane Addams, and Jeannette Rankin. On the lines below, write one interesting fact or anecdote about each woman that you might include in your history tour. Record additional information in the on-screen Notebook.

Elizabeth Cady Stanton: _____

_____

Jane Addams: _____

_____

Jeannette Rankin: _____

_____

5. Your tour will be more interesting if you illustrate it. Go to the Report Maker and access the Image Library. Look through the library and choose illustrations for your tour. List the pictures on the lines below.

_____

_____

_____

6. You will also need an inviting beginning for your history tour. Write a sample opening on the lines below. Try to arouse the audience's attention so that they will want to continue on the tour.

_____

_____

_____

7. Compile the notes and other information that you have collected. Use the Report Maker to draft the text for your history tour. Then attach the pictures you have selected from the Image Library. Ask a classmate to read your draft and suggest revisions. After revising and editing your work, share it with the class.

CD-ROM Explorer

ACTIVITY 22
Overseas Expansion

In this activity, you will draw a political cartoon about American overseas expansion before 1914. The CD-ROM *American Heritage® History of the United States* will help you research the topic. Use this guide to track your exploration.

1. In the Time Capsule, go to the Time Tour and access the chapter "Expanding Overseas." (For help in locating the chapter, consult the detailed Time Tour Contents on page 90 of this Guidebook.) Read the chapter carefully. Click the blue hot spots to listen to the audio. As you read and listen, take notes in the on-screen Notebook.

2. Scroll through the chapter again, watching for the icons that indicate a map is available. Click the map icons and study the three maps showing United States expansion in this period. Makes notes in the on-screen Notebook.

3. Use the left scroll-out menu to access History Makers. Then read the biography of Alfred T. Mahan. On the lines below, identify at least three of Mahan's ideas that influenced the expansion of the United States. Take more detailed notes in the on-screen Notebook.

   1. _____

      _____

   2. _____

      _____

   3. _____

      _____

4. Next, use the left scroll-out menu to access Presidents. Read the biography of Theodore Roosevelt. On the lines below, note at least two expansionist events in which Roosevelt played an important role. Take additional notes in the on-screen Notebook.

   _____

   _____

5. Review your notes. Then brainstorm a list of possible topics and messages for a political cartoon about American expansion on the lines below. Put a check next to the topic and message that you will use for your cartoon.

Topic	Message
______________________	______________________________
______________________	______________________________
______________________	______________________________
______________________	______________________________

6. Draw a first sketch of your political cartoon on American overseas expansion before 1914 in the space below. Be sure to include a title and any necessary text in your drawing.

7. Ask a partner to suggest ways you can revise and improve your sketch. Then draw a final version of your cartoon and share it with the class.

 # CD-ROM Explorer

ACTIVITY 23
World War I on the Home Front

What was it like to be an American on the home front during World War I? In this activity, you will create a scrapbook of an American who lived through the war. The CD-ROM *American Heritage® History of the United States* will help you get started on your research. Use this guide to track your exploration.

1. In the Time Capsule, go to the Time Tour and access the chapter "World War I." (For help in locating the chapter on the CD-ROM, consult the detailed Time Tour Contents on page 90 of this Guidebook.) Read the chapter. Pay special attention to the subsection "Organizing the War Effort." As you read, click the blue hot spot to listen to the audio about the Harlem Hell Fighters. Click the video control button to watch the video footage of World War I. Take notes in the on-screen Notebook.

2. While you are in the Time Tour chapter "World War I," click the map icons to access the maps "Europe in World War I" and "The Western Front." Why would such maps be of interest to Americans on the home front? Write your ideas on the lines below.

_____

_____

_____

3. Use the left scroll-out menu to access History Makers. Locate and read the biography of Jeannette Rankin. Take notes in the Notebook.

4. Now it is time to decide the identity of the American whose scrapbook you will create. Will you put together the scrapbook of a teenager? Of an old man who fought in the Civil War? Of the wife of a soldier fighting in Europe? Identify the person you have selected and his or her point of view about the war on the lines below.

Identity: _____

Point of View: _____

_____

_____

5. What kind of entries will you include in your scrapbook? You should plan on at least five different types. These might include letters to and from a relative who is a soldier, newspaper or magazine articles, maps, pictures, words of a song, poems, advertisements for a show, or diary entries. On the lines below, list five entries that you will use.

_____

_____

_____

_____

_____

6. To find pictures for your scrapbook, go to the Report Maker and access the Image Library. Explore the library, and then list at least two pictures that you might use in your scrapbook on the lines below.

_____

_____

7. Now you are ready to create your scrapbook. Make sure that the entries reflect the identity of your character, including your character's position on the war. Write and assemble the materials you will use. Use the Report Maker to draft and polish your work.

★ ★ ★ ★ ★ ★ ★ ★ ★ ★ ★ ★ ★ ★ ★ ★

CD-ROM Explorer

ACTIVITY 24
The Jazz Age

This activity will help you find out more about jazz, a key musical development of the Roaring Twenties. Follow the guide below to prepare a five-minute presentation about jazz. The CD-ROM *American Heritage® History of the United States* will help you research the topic. Use this guide to track your exploration.

1. In the right scroll-out menu, click the Index and then search to find references to jazz. List the references below.

   _____

   _____

   _____

2. Explore the jazz references one by one. Take notes in the on-screen Notebook as you read and listen to the material. Make sure to access the video footage of people dancing the Charleston. Use the red hot spots in each article to browse other parts of the CD-ROM for information.

3. Go to the Report Maker and access the Image Library. List pictures that you might want to include in your presentation on the lines below.

   _____

   _____

4. You are now ready to focus your research. For example, do you want to present an overview of jazz in the 1920s? Concentrate on a particular jazz artist? Compare jazz to another musical form of the period? Or compare the jazz of the 1920s to jazz today? Use the space below to describe the focus of your presentation.

   _____

   _____

   _____

   _____

   _____

5. Go to the Internet by quitting the program and launching your web browser. In the location field, type http://www.yahoo.com. Use Yahoo to find a list of search engines. Use different engines to search for information about jazz. On the lines below, list key words and addresses that resulted in helpful information. Add new facts to the on-screen Notebook.

Key Words: _____

_____

_____

Addresses: _____

_____

_____

_____

_____

6. Now compile the information that you have gathered about jazz. Create a brief outline of your presentation that includes possible visual and audio elements.

7. Use your outline to write the text for your presentation in the Report Maker. After reviewing and editing this text, practice giving your presentation. Make sure to time yourself so that you do not run over five minutes. When you feel ready, give your presentation to the class.

★ ★ ★ ★ ★ ★ ★ ★ ★ ★ ★ ★ ★ ★ ★

CD-ROM Explorer

ACTIVITY 25
The New Deal

President Roosevelt's New Deal resulted in great changes in Americans' lives. In this activity, you will write a script for an imaginary "fireside chat" about the New Deal. Roosevelt gave these informal radio speeches to keep the public informed about what he was doing. In your fireside chat, you will explain how you believe the New Deal will benefit Americans. The CD-ROM *American Heritage® History of the United States* will help you research the topic. Use this guide to track your exploration.

1. In the Time Tour, access the chapter "Depression and the New Deal." (To help locate the chapter, consult the detailed Time Tour Contents on page 90 of this Guidebook.) As you read the chapter, pay special attention to the section "FDR and the New Deal." Also, be sure to listen to the excerpt from John Steinbeck's *The Grapes of Wrath*. Take research notes in the on-screen Notebook.

2. Scroll through "FDR and the New Deal" to the subsection "A Bold Experiment." Reread the subsection. As you read, click the icon to access and study the map "Tennessee Valley Authority." Make notes in the on-screen Notebook. Then write a statement that you might make about the TVA project on the lines below.

_____

_____

_____

3. Now reread the subsection "Drought and Dust" and study the map "The Dust Bowl." Make notes in the on-screen Notebook. On the lines below, list the problems created by dust storms in the 1930s and explain the hardships they brought to people who lived in the region of the Dust Bowl.

_____

_____

_____

_____

4. In the left scroll-out menu, access Presidents. Then locate and read the biography of Franklin D. Roosevelt. On the lines below, list at least two actions that Roosevelt took as part of the New Deal. Take additional research notes in the on-screen Notebook.

_____

_____

_____

5. Decide on a focus for your fireside chat. You might describe the terrible conditions caused by the Depression or the Dust Bowl, discuss the New Deal as a whole, or explain specific programs such as the TVA project. Summarize the focus of your fireside chat below.

_____

_____

_____

6. You will need to begin your fireside chat with a powerful statement. What words might you use to get people's attention? On the lines below, write your ideas for an opening statement.

_____

_____

_____

7. Compile the information that you have gathered. Write a draft script of your fireside chat in the Report Maker. Read the script to a partner and ask for suggestions. After making revisions, prepare a final version of your speech. You may want to record your fireside chat on an audio tape and play it for the class.

 CD-ROM Explorer

ACTIVITY 26
A Global War

In this activity, you will write an outline for a television documentary about World War II. The CD-ROM *American Heritage® History of the United States* will help you research information for the documentary. Use this guide to track your exploration.

1. Use the left scroll-out menu to access the Time Tour unit "Prosperity, Depression, and War." When the unit collage appears, click the chapter "World War II." Explore the chapter carefully. Be sure to access the audio and video materials. On the lines below, list at least three events from the war that you might include in your documentary. Take additional research notes in the on-screen Notebook.

_____

_____

_____

2. In the Time Capsule, access the Presidents section. Locate and read the biographies of Franklin Roosevelt and Harry Truman. Write one fact about the role of each President during World War II on the lines below. Take additional notes in the on-screen Notebook.

Franklin Roosevelt: _____

_____

Harry Truman: _____

_____

3. Decide on a topic for your television documentary. You might create a program about D-Day or about the war in the Pacific. Or you might document events on the home front, such as the experiences of a woman worker in a war industry. Describe the topic of your documentary below.

_____

_____

_____

4. Go to the Internet by quitting the program and launching your web browser. In the location field, type http://www.yahoo.com. Use Yahoo to find a list of search engines. Use different search engines to search for information about World War II relating to the topic of your documentary. On the lines below, list key words and addresses that resulted in helpful information. Add new facts to the on-screen Notebook.

Key Words: _____

_____

_____

Addresses: _____

_____

_____

_____

_____

5. Collect the notes that you have assembled. Use the Report Maker to draft an outline for your television documentary. Explore the Image Library in the Report Maker and attach pictures you might use to illustrate the program. You might also scroll through the "World War II" chapter for ideas about suitable video footage. Describe the footage you would like to include in your outline.

 **CD-ROM Explorer**

ACTIVITY 27
The Cold War

In this activity, you will develop a multiple-choice game about the Cold War. The CD-ROM *American Heritage® History of the United States* will help you research facts for the game. Use this guide to track your exploration.

1. Your game will be called "Who Am I? What Am I?" In the on-screen Notebook, write the headings "Who" and "What." You will use these categories to organize the notes you take while exploring the *History of the United States* CD-ROM.

2. In the Time Capsule, go to the Time Tour and access the chapter "The Fifties." (For help in locating the chapter, consult the detailed Time Tour Contents on page 90 of this Guidebook.) Read the first two sections of the chapter: "The Nation Faces a Cold War" and "The Cold War Turns Hot." As you read, be sure to access the video materials. Take notes for questions about the Cold War under the "Who" and "What" headings in the on-screen Notebook.

3. Use the left scroll-out menu to access Face the Issues. Then click "Vietnam War" to explore the CD-ROM feature about this Cold War event. List at least three people, places, and events or ideas related to the Vietnam War in the chart below. Take additional notes in the on-screen Notebook.

People	Places	Events/Ideas
_____	_____	_____
_____	_____	_____
_____	_____	_____
_____	_____	_____
_____	_____	_____
_____	_____	_____
_____	_____	_____
_____	_____	_____

4. Use the left scroll-out menu to access Presidents. Locate and read the following biographies: Harry Truman, Dwight Eisenhower, John Kennedy, Lyndon Johnson, and Richard Nixon. Write a multiple-choice question about the role of one of these Presidents in the Cold War below. Add notes for additional questions about the Presidents under the "Who" and "What" headings in the on-screen Notebook.

   Question: _____

   _____

   a. _____

   b. _____

   c. _____

5. Access History Makers and read the biography of Maya Lin. Based on the biography, write a question about the Cold War on the lines below. Take notes for additional questions in the on-screen Notebook.

   Question: _____

   _____

   a. _____

   b. _____

   c. _____

6. Review the notes you have taken. Then use the Report Maker to draft the final questions for your game. The game should include at least 15 multiple-choice questions. Be sure to keep a record of the answers. When you are done, create a system for scoring your game. Then have two teams play the game to test their knowledge of the Cold War.

★ ★ ★ ★ ★ ★ ★ ★ ★ ★ ★ ★ ★ ★ ★ ★

 **CD-ROM Explorer**

ACTIVITY 28
Civil Rights

In this activity, you will write a short story about the civil rights movement. The CD-ROM *American Heritage® History of the United States* will help you research the subject. Use this guide to track your exploration.

1. One of the landmarks in the civil rights movement was the Supreme Court case of *Brown* v. *Board of Education of Topeka*. In the Time Capsule, go to Face the Issues and access *"Brown* v. *Board of Education."* Read through the material. Then, on the lines below, list three people and the position of each on integrated public education. Take notes in the on-screen Notebook.

Person   Position

_____   _____

_____   _____

_____   _____

2. Access the Index in the right scroll-out menu. Use the Index to locate material on civil rights. You might also search key words and phrases such as *segregation, National Association for the Advancement of Colored People (NAACP), Southern Christian Leadership Conference (SCLC), Freedom Riders, National Farm Workers Association, American Indian Movement (AIM), National Organization for Women (NOW),* and *Equal Pay Act of 1963.* Click the Index entries and read the material. As you read, be sure to access the audio and visual material, as well. Take notes in the Notebook.

3. Use the left scroll-out menu to access History Makers. Locate and read the following biographies: Thurgood Marshall, Cesar Chavez, and Martin Luther King, Jr. On the lines below, list one key fact about the role of each history maker in the civil rights movement. Take additional notes about these leaders in the on-screen Notebook.

Marshall: _____

Chavez: _____

King: _____

4. Return to the left scroll-out menu and access Arts and Entertainment. Scroll through to the Music section and read about the role folk music played in the civil rights movement. Add notes to the on-screen Notebook.

5. In the Report Maker, access the Image Library. Look through the images that relate to the civil rights movement. On the lines below, note at least three pictures that might spark ideas for a story or that you might use to illustrate a story about civil rights.

_____

_____

_____

6. Now you are ready to begin your story. Compile the notes and other information that you have gathered. Then, in the space below, list the main story elements you will use.

Characters: _____

_____

_____

Setting: _____

_____

_____

Historical Details: _____

_____

_____

7. Use the Report Maker to write your story. Attach any pictures you have selected from the Image Library. After revising and editing your story, you may wish to share it with the class.

Name _____ Class _____ Date _____

 **CD-ROM Explorer**

ACTIVITY 29
A Changing World

In this activity, you will create a poster about the world after the Cold War. The CD-ROM *American Heritage® History of the United States* will help you research the topic. Use this guide to track your exploration.

1. In the Time Capsule, go to the Time Tour and access the chapter "New Directions." (For help in locating the chapter, consult the detailed Time Tour Contents on page 90 in this Guidebook.) As you read the chapter, pay special attention to the section "An End to the Cold War." Take research notes in the on-screen Notebook.

2. Go to the Internet by quitting the program and launching your web browser. In the location field, type http://www.yahoo.com. Use Yahoo to find a list of search engines to search for information on the end of the Cold War. On the lines below, list key words and addresses that resulted in helpful information. Add new facts to the on-screen Notebook.

   Key Words: _____

   _____

   Addresses: _____

   _____

   _____

   _____

3. Decide the focus of your poster. Will it celebrate the end of the Cold War? Or will it highlight the current problems in Eastern Europe and the former Soviet Union? Write your decision below.

   _____

   _____

   _____

   _____

4. Based on the focus you selected, think of at least five images that you will use to communicate your message in the poster. Remember, you can use pictures cut from magazines, original drawings, maps, newspaper clippings, and so on. List the images below.

_____

_____

_____

_____

_____

5. What text will you use in your poster? The text can include a title, slogans, descriptions of the images, words in balloons, and so on. Write a first draft of the text in the Report Maker. Then draw a rough sketch of your poster in the space below.

6. Ask a partner to suggest ways you can improve your poster. Then create a final version and share it with the class.

 **CD-ROM Explorer**

ACTIVITY 30
Toward the Future

When you study history, you spend a lot of time looking at the past. But sometimes history gives you clues about the future, too. In this activity, you will explore two homes of the past. Using the CD-ROM *American Heritage® History of the United States*, you will then make predictions about a home of the future. Use this guide to track your exploration.

1. Enter the Time Capsule and access Virtual Buildings. Once you are in Virtual Buildings, explore the Log Cabin. On the lines below, make notes about a log cabin home and the lives of the people who lived there.

   Design or Plan: _____

   Furniture: _____

   Food and Cooking: _____

   Clothing: _____

   Energy Sources: _____

   Toys: _____

   Entertainment: _____

2. Next, visit the 1950s Suburban Home. Make notes about a 1950s home on the lines below.

   Design or Plan: _____

   Furniture: _____

   Appliances: _____

   Food and Cooking: _____

   Clothing: _____

   Energy Sources: _____

   Toys: _____

   Entertainment: _____

   Communication: _____

3. Now, think about a present-day home. How is it similar to a 1950s home? How is it different? List at least three similarities and three differences on the lines below.

Similarities   Differences

_____   _____

_____   _____

_____   _____

4. Go to the Time Tour and access the chapter "Toward a New Century." (For help in locating the chapter, consult the detailed Time Tour Contents on page 90 of this Guidebook.) As you read the chapter, think about how new technology and environmental concerns might affect the way future Americans live. Take notes in the on-screen Notebook.

5. In the Report Maker, write a description of a home of the future as you imagine it. Use the list of topics in questions 1 and 2 above as a guide for your description. Then, in the space below, draw a floor plan for your house. Label the items inside the house. If they are new and unfamiliar items, describe what they are and explain how they work.

CD-ROM Explorer

ACTIVITY 31
Civics Overview: American Democracy

It is important for Americans to understand the workings of the national government. In this assignment, you will plan a virtual tour of one branch of the national government—the legislative branch, the executive branch, or the judicial branch. The CD-ROM *American Heritage® History of the United States* will help you access on-line information about the national government. Use this guide to track your exploration.

1. In the Time Capsule, go to the Time Tour and access the chapter "Creating a Republic." (For help in locating the chapter, consult the detailed Time Tour Contents on page 90 of this Guidebook.) Read the section "Separation of Powers." Take research notes in the on-screen Notebook.

2. Decide which branch of government will be the focus of your virtual tour—legislative, executive, or judicial. Write your decision below.

_____

3. Go to the Internet by quitting the program and launching your web browser. In the location field, type http://www.yahoo.com. Use Yahoo to find a list of search engines. Use different search engines to find information about the government branch you chose. As you explore, list addresses that you might include in your virtual tour on the lines below. Add new facts to the on-screen Notebook.

Addresses: _____

_____

_____

_____

_____

_____

_____

_____

_____

4. Now that you have explored the sites that are already on-line, think about creating your own on-line tour of the government. What information will you cover? What visual or audio elements will you include? How will your virtual tour encourage participation in democracy? Write your ideas below.

_____

_____

_____

5. Review your notes in the Notebook. Then create an outline for your virtual tour in the Report Maker. The tour should contain a homepage, at least three pages of information about your chosen branch of government, and a page listing other sites with information about the government branch. In the space below, create a diagram showing how your pages are organized.

Answer Key

Activity 1
American Rivers
1. Notes should contain information on at least five major rivers of North America. Possible answers: Ohio—begins in Appalachians, runs through the Central Plains, and joins the Mississippi; Mississippi—begins in Minnesota, runs through the Central Plains, and empties into the Gulf of Mexico; Missouri—begins in the Rockies, runs through northern Great Plains, and joins the Mississippi; Colorado River—begins in the Rockies, runs through Colorado, Utah, Nevada, and California, and empties into the Gulf of California; Rio Grande—begins in the Rockies, runs south, forms part of the border of the United States and Mexico, and empties into the Gulf of Mexico. **2.** Answer should include the river(s) covered, the theme of the documentary, and the point of view in the narrative.
3. Students should list key words and at least two addresses of useful sites. Encourage them to print out important information and images. **4.** Students should write at least three main points for their documentary. You may want to check these points before they write the outlines. **5.** Use the following guidelines to evaluate the documentary outline: Is the information accurate? Is it presented in an interesting and logical way? Does the presen-tation make good use of the material available, in-cluding visual and audio references?

Activity 2
The Incas
1. Location: by 1492, the Inca empire stretched for almost 3,000 miles along the western coast of South America. Possible notes: largest empire in the Americas; important advances in agriculture, engineering, and medicine. **2.** Students should list key words and at least two addresses of useful sites. One category of useful sites is travel agencies advertising trips to see Inca ruins in Peru. **3.** Places, people or events, foods, and recreation should accurately reflect information on the Incas. Possible answers: places—Macchu Picchu, Cuzco; people or events—Pachacuti, the founder of the Incan empire, or the founding of the Inca empire in 1438, the civil war following the death of Huayna Capac in 1525, Atahualpa, the last Incan ruler, or the Spanish invasion in 1532; foods—corn, pota-toes, squash, beans, tortillas, seafood, roasted meat; recreation—festivals, dances, feasts, sports, games. **4.** You might wish to provide students with sample travel brochures to help them get ideas for organ-ization and layout. **5.** Use the following guidelines to evaluate brochures: Is the information accurate? Is it presented in a colorful and appealing way? Did the student show awareness of audience in creating the brochure? Does the brochure reflect skill and creativity in conducting and presenting research?

Activity 3
Trade in New France
1. Notes should include Samuel de Champlain and European rivalry over the fur trade. **2.** Pos-sible characters: coureurs de bois, Indian wife, Indian trappers, French merchants, Algonquin ally or Iroquois rival. **3.** Notes should include at least two details from the Iroquois longhouse. Possible details: canoes were constructed from elm tree bark and large canoes could carry up to 30 people; a staple food was corn; meat and fish were eaten fresh, or dried and smoked; buckskin was made by soaking the hide in a mixture of deer brains to soften it, tying it to a frame to stretch it, and smoking it over a fire to strengthen it; clothes and moccasins were made of buckskin; snowshoes allowed travel through deep snow. **4.** Decisions for each element should reflect the historical background of the topic. **5.** Use the following guidelines to evaluate stories: Is the historical information accurate? Does the story include historical characters, an authentic setting, and accurate details? Does the story reflect skill and creativity in assessing and utilizing research?

Activity 4
The English Colonies
1. Notes should reflect information found in the Time Tour on the English colonies. **2.** New Eng-land: Massachusetts (including Maine), Connect-icut, Rhode Island, New Hampshire; Middle: New York, Delaware, New Jersey, Pennsylvania; South-ern: Maryland, Virginia, North Carolina, South Carolina, Georgia. **3.** Notes should cover each his-tory maker listed. **4.** Possible notes: Music: hymns; European folk songs; and African songs, including "call and response" pattern. Literature: Bible; *Pil-grim's Progress* by John Bunyan; poetry of Anne Bradstreet; published sermons. **5.** Questions should be answerable from the CD-ROM. **6.** Use the fol-lowing guidelines to evaluate games: Are the ques-tions interesting and well-researched? Do they reflect a sound understanding of the topic? Did students make good use of the CD-ROM research possibilities? Can the questions be answered by using the CD-ROM?

Activity 5
British Policies in the American Colonies
1. Notes should reflect information found in the Time Tour. **2.** References found through red hot spots should be listed. Possible references: Patrick Henry, Benjamin Franklin, and Abigail Adams. **3.** Students should choose three issues from their brainstorming list. Issues might include: loyalty to Britain, Stamp Act, Townshend Acts, Sons and Daughters of Liberty, Boston Massacre, Boston Tea

Party, Intolerable Acts, first Continental Congress, battles of Lexington and Concord. **4.** Questions should reflect an understanding of the issues chosen. **5.** Point of view on issues should reflect whether the colonist is a patriot, a loyalist, or undecided. Example: If the colonist is a patriot and the issue is the Boston Tea Party, the point of view would be that it was a brave act that showed Britain that the colonists would not back down. **6.** Use the following guidelines to evaluate interviews: Are the questions and answers well researched? Do they reflect the issues of the period? Are they organized in a logical way? **7.** You may wish to give students extra credit for polished performances of the interview.

Activity 6
The Continental Army
1. Students should list references to the Continental Army. **2.** Notes should reflect information in the Time Tour. **3.** Notes should describe George Washington's role in leading the Continental Army to victory and mention that James Monroe and Andrew Jackson served in this army. **4.** Alexander Hamilton became a captain in the Continental Army at age 19 and his troops were very well-disciplined. Washington asked Hamilton to join his personal staff. John Marshall joined the Virginia militia and spent three years in the Continental Army. **5.** You may wish to check these sentences before students begin writing their articles. **6.** Possible images: George Washington, Battle of Bunker Hill, Continental Army soldiers, Revolutionary motto, Battle of Lexington, Cornwallis surrenders. **7.** Use the following guidelines to evaluate articles: Is the information accurate? Does the article reflect good research skills and demonstrate an understanding of the information on the CD-ROM? Is the article well-organized and thought-out? Is the article carefully written?

Activity 7
The Constitutional Convention
1. Students should list references to the Articles of the Confederation and the Constitutional Convention. **2.** Notes should reflect the material in the Time Tour. **3.** Possible answer: Franklin might have said something about compromising. Although he refused to attend the convention, Henry might have said something about the right of individuals versus the states. Hamilton would have supported a strong, centralized government. Madison might have shared some of his research or urged the states to ratify the Constitution. **4.** Notes should reflect the material in Face the Issues. **5.** Students should decide on the characters and issues. Issues might include: lack of power and authority of national government; need to protect interests of states; Virginia Plan—proportional representation, favored by larger states; New Jersey Plan—gives states an equal number of votes, favored by smaller states; two-house legislature, with proportional representation in one

house and equal representation in the other house. **6–7.** Use the following guidelines to evaluate the script: Does it accurately reflect different points of view? Does it demonstrate a good understanding of the issues the members of the convention faced? Is it presented in an interesting way?

Activity 8
Election of 1800
1. Students should find references for: election of 1800, events leading up to election, Democratic-Republican party, Federalist party, Thomas Jefferson, Aaron Burr. **2.** Notes should reflect information in the Time Tour. **3.** Jefferson believed more political power should belong to the states and to ordinary citizens. He and Hamilton were in constant conflict. Jefferson and his supporters formed the Democratic-Republicans. Jefferson became Vice President in 1796. In 1800, Jefferson ran for President against Aaron Burr and the incumbent John Adams and won. **4.** Hamilton supported a strong, centralized government. He proposed: that the national government take over all state debts; taxation to raise money for the national government; and establishment of a national bank. He was the head of the Federalist party. When it became apparent that neither Federalist candidate would win the election of 1800, Hamilton threw his influence behind Jefferson rather than Burr. **5.** Students should list a political party and include two or three facts about it. Example: Federalists—raised taxes for war; led by Hamilton; favored strong federal government. **6.** Message will vary, but should accurately reflect party of choice. **7.** Possible images: Hamilton, Jefferson, Bank of the United States. **8.** You may wish to show students the homepages of current political candidates before they start writing. Use the following guidelines to evaluate homepages: Is it historically accurate? Does the student show creativity in presenting the material? Does the presentation reflect skill and thoroughness in researching material?

Activity 9
Lewis and Clark
1. Students should find references for Lewis and Clark, Louisiana Purchase, and Sacajawea. **2.** Possible answers: Missouri, Snake, and Columbia rivers; Rocky Mountains, Bitterroot Range; Continental Divide, Great Falls. **3.** Notes should contain relevant information about Lewis and Clark. **4.** Characters, setting, and events should reflect historical and geographic accuracy. Example: characters—Lewis, Clark, Sacajawea, other explorers; setting—the mouth of the Columbia River on the Pacific; event—the first sighting of the Pacific. **5.** Use the following guidelines to evaluate movie scenes: Does it reflect careful research? Is it historically accurate? Does it demonstrate a good understanding of the exploration? Is it presented in an interesting way? Does the storyboard parallel the script?

Activity 10
The Industrial Revolution

1. Students should find references for: the Industrial Revolution, inventions, steamboats, John Deere, Cyrus McCormick, and Samuel F.B. Morse. **2.** Students should demonstrate an awareness of text and audio material on CD-ROM. **3.** Students should list at least three of the following canals: Erie, Champlain, Chesapeake and Ohio, Pennsylvania, James and Kanawha, Ohio and Erie, Wabash and Erie, Miami and Erie, Illinois and Michigan. **4.** Encourage students to list topics without judging them until after the brainstorming session is complete. Possible topics: growth of cities; inventions, such as spinning jenny, power loom, cotton gin, telegraph, reaper, steel plow; growth of factories, such as textile mills; poor working conditions in factories; building a canal; changes in transportation including canals, steamboats, and railroads allow the mass movement of people. **5.** Use the following guidelines to evaluate murals: Does the mural show topics related to the early stages of the Industrial Revolution? Does the mural reflect research on the CD-ROM? Are the images depicted historically accurate? Is the mural skillfully executed?

Activity 11
The Age of Andrew Jackson

1. Information might include: Jackson grew up on the frontier and thus might appreciate the way of life of Native Americans; Jackson fought the Creek and Seminole Indians; he favored the Indian Removal Act. **2.** Possible answer: Jackson might discuss Indian removal to the west, life on the frontier, or his Indian-fighting days. **3.** Possible answer: Sequoyah might discuss their experiences in the War of 1812, the Trail of Tears, his attempt to preserve his culture by creating a Cherokee alphabet, or the United States government's failure to honor treaties. **4.** Notes should include information on the Cherokees, the Indian Removal Act, and the Trail of Tears. **5.** Possible answers: *Indian removal*: Jackson—Native Americans have to get out of the way of progress. There is other land for you to live on in the west. Sequoyah—The "civilized" tribes are like the whites. The Cherokees have adapted so that they can live in harmony with the whites. Why can't they stay in the East? You said yourself that "the poor and humble require the arm and shield of the law." *War of 1812*: Jackson: I was a great officer. Sequoyah—I fought alongside you to protect this nation. Don't I and my people deserve to be treated better? **6.** Possible answers: Jackson's attitude—superior, believing he is right; Sequoyah's attitude—proud, angry (because his people are being hurt), or reasonable (using logical arguments to support his views). **7.** Use the following guide-lines to evaluate conversations: Does it reflect accurate understanding of the lives and backgrounds of Jackson and Sequoyah? Is the dialogue realistic? Does it reflect research on the CD-ROM?

Activity 12
On the Oregon Trail

1. Notes should reflect information about Oregon Country. **2.** Possible answers: rivers—Platte, Snake, Columbia, Willamette; landform—Rocky Mountains. **3.** Notes might include: beginning—Independence, Missouri; ending—Oregon; length—about 2,000 miles; trail that crosses it—Mormon Trail; trails that split off from it—California Trail; communities or landmarks—Ft. Laramie, South Pass, Ft. Walla Walla. **4.** Possible answers: Great Plains: Cheyenne, Dakota, Mandan, Crow—hunted buffalo; built sod houses and used tepees; farmed along rivers; in the mid-1700s, used horses. Plateau: Nez Percé—lived between Rocky Mountains and Cascades; main source of food was fish; lived in earth houses that were partly underground. Northwest Coast: Kwakiutl—favorable climate with abundant food; fish from sea and meat from forest animals; built permanent villages and traded with other groups. (Answers might also include eastern Native American groups that had been removed to Indian Territory, such as the Cherokees.) **5.** Because he knew about many different Native American cultures, Catlin might have told the pioneers how to avoid hostilities, such as not killing too many buffalo. He might have urged pioneers to respect Native Americans and their cultures. **6.** Students should list key words and at least two addresses of useful sites. **7.** "Home on the Range," "Shenandoah," "My Darling Clementine," "Whoopie Ti Yi Yo." **8.** Use the following guidelines to evaluate letters: Is the letter historically and geographically accurate? Did the writer include sufficient details and use research material creatively? Is the letter well-organized? Does it follow a conventional form?

Activity 13
The Cotton Kingdom

1. Notes should reflect information about the Cotton Kingdom. **2.** Textiles, iron and steel, mining, lumber, tobacco, cattle, rice and sugar cane, cotton, grain **3.** Possible statements: Stowe—The institution of slavery in the Cotton Kingdom is evil, and the Fugitive Slave Act encourages it. I will try to arouse public opinion against these evils by writing a book about them. Tubman—Life for those of us who are enslaved in the South is unbearable, and the people I helped escape were willing to risk death for their freedom. Douglass—My boyhood was spent sleeping on a damp dirt floor and I often went without food or clothing. Slavery in the Cotton Kingdom is inhumane and must be abolished. **4.** Music: call and response; spirituals. Book: *Narrative of the Life of Frederick Douglass, an American Slave*; *Uncle Tom's Cabin*. **5.** Possible images: enslaved African Americans on a plantation, slave auction. **6.** You might wish to check students' notes before they create their presentation. **7.** Use these guidelines to evaluate dramatic presentations: Did students use historically accurate information? Did students show creativity in planning their presentation? Did students make good use of their research?

Activity 14
The Underground Railroad

1. Notes should reflect information about the anti-slavery movement. **2.** Possible questions: Tubman—What was your closest escape on the underground railroad? Douglass—Can you describe how runaway slaves made their way to your home as a stop on the underground railroad? **3.** Possible answers: Feelings—fear; elation; weariness. Problems—getting caught; getting killed; getting lost; hunger; cold. **4.** Spirituals used in escape: "Steal Away," "Swing Low, Sweet Chariot." Possible spirituals to research: "Deep River," "Go Down, Moses," "Roll, Jordan Roll." **5.** Possible answers: Tubman—her dedication to helping other slaves escape; Douglass—use of newspaper to enlist support for abolition; escaping slave—description of an escape. **6.** Use the following guidelines to evaluate conversations: Do the questions demonstrate a good understanding of the underground railroad? Has the student shown skill and creativity in writing the conversation? Is the conversation based on historical facts?

Activity 15
Slavery in the Western Territories

1. Notes should reflect information about the issue of slavery between 1820 and 1861. **2.** Possible answers: Clay—determined to keep nation intact, despite the slavery issue; Calhoun—believed that southern slaveowners had rights and that fugitive slaves should be returned to them; he also believed that slavery should be allowed in the western territories; Charles Beecher—felt that slavery was a sin. **3.** Possible notes: Clay—helped work out Missouri Compromise in 1820 and argued for the Compromise of 1850. Douglass—lectured against slavery, wrote his autobiography *Narrative of the Life of Frederick Douglass, an American Slave* and other articles, founded anti-slavery newspaper *North Star.* **4.** Taylor—Compromise of 1850, against it; Fillmore—Compromise of 1850, supported it; Pierce—Kansas-Nebraska Act, supported it; Buchanan—violence in Kansas, Dred Scott decision, John Brown's raid, opposed slavery but did not believe that the national government should dictate the decisions of individual states. **5.** Use the following guidelines to evaluate paragraphs: Did students include key events during each President's term of office? Are their paragraphs well-organized and coherently presented? Do they reflect careful research?

Activity 16
The Blue and the Gray

1. Notes should reflect CD-ROM material on the Civil War, including the audio clips of President Lincoln's speeches. **2.** Possible answers: Union—Wilderness, Siege of Petersburg. Confederate—Spotsylvania, Cold Harbor. **3.** Possible notes: Lee—took over the Confederate Army in 1862 and won a series of brilliant strategic victories; surrendered to General Grant at Appo-mattox on April 9, 1865. Barton—gathered medical supplies, then operated as a one-woman nursing unit; after the war, set up a system to look for missing soldiers. **4.** Possible notes: Lincoln—by the time he was inaugurated, the South had become the Confederate States of America; Civil War began; issued the Emancipation Proclamation in 1863; gave Gettysburg Address in 1863; finally selected Ulysses S. Grant as General to lead the northern armies; Civil War ended on April 9, 1865; Lincoln was shot and killed five days later. **5.** Movie: *The Birth of a Nation*; Book: *The Red Badge of Courage*; Songs: "Dixie," "The Battle Hymn of the Republic," "John Brown's Body" **6.** Students should state the form of memorial and the person(s) or event commemorated. **7–8.** Use the following guidelines to evaluate memorials and dedication speeches: Did the student show creativity in making, drawing, or describing the memorial? Does the memorial and the speech demonstrate a clear understanding of the history involved? Did students make good use of the research they did?

Activity 17
Reconstruction

1. Notes should reflect information about Reconstruction. **2.** Andrew Johnson, Ulysses Grant, Rutherford Hayes **3.** Possible answers: Revels—first African American to serve in Congress; was Senator for Mississippi for a one-year term; voted for amnesty for former Confederate officers; supported school integration in the District of Columbia and enforcement of the Fifteenth Amendment. **4.** Possible answers: Johnson; Grant; Hayes; Revels; African American congressmen; Suffrage for African Americans. **5.** Students should identify kinds of test questions and write two sample questions and answers. Examples: A leader of the Radicals in the House was (Thaddeus Stevens). How did the southern states prevent African Americans from exerting the rights spelled out in the Thirteenth Amendment? (They passed black codes that severely limited the rights of the freedmen.) **6.** Use the following guidelines to evaluate tests: Do the questions cover the important events and issues of Reconstruction? Are the questions clearly worded? Do students know the answers to the questions they are asking? Can other students complete the test with reasonable success?

Activity 18
On the Plains

1. Notes should reflect information about farming on the Plains. Check to make sure students list other references. **2.** Students should locate their farms in a state or territory in the Great Plains. **3.** Students should list a character and at least two activities. **4.** Possible: Cooking—cooked over fire in cast iron pots; biggest meal at noon; grew, raised, or hunted almost all food; Furnishings—simple, handmade benches, settles, chairs; spinning wheel; bed warmers; Chores—farming; cooking; spinning; knitting; sewing; washing clothes; minding children; gardening; making candles; making soap; taking care of animals. **5.** "Home on the Range," "Shenandoah" **6.** Possible images: buffalo, pioneers **7.** Use the following guidelines to evaluate diary entries:

Is the information historically and geographically accurate? Does the diary entry demonstrate a good understanding of farming life on the Great Plains? Did the student show skill and creativity in constructing the diary entry?

Activity 19
Business and Industry
1. Notes should reflect information about industrial growth in the United States, including reactions to the video footage of factories and the Model T. **2.** Carnegie—built up steel industry in the United States; Gompers—founded and led the American Federation of Labor (AFL), a large labor union formed to protect skilled workers; Ford—revolutionized automaking by introducing the assembly line; Tarbell—exposed abuses in oil industry and big business; Edison—opened an "invention factory" where he and dozens of scientists developed the most important machines of the age, including the phonograph and the electric light bulb; he also set up the electric power company that lit New York City. **3.** For: helped poor families by employing children, kept costs for employers down; Against: exploited children, prevented adults from getting jobs, drove down salaries, kept children from attending school which limited their future career options, weakened parental discipline and led to the breakdown of the family. **4.** The point of view should match the history maker that students chose. **5–6.** Use the following guidelines to evaluate editorials: Did the writer state the issue and his or her position clearly? Has the writer supported the position with details, examples, and arguments? Does the paper reflect good research and an understanding of the issue? Is the paper well-organized and presented in a logical way?

Activity 20
In the City
1. Check to see that students follow directions on how to set up their notes. **2.** Notes should reflect information about lives of poor and middle class in American cities in the late 1800s and early 1900s, including notes on the video and audio material. **3.** Set up Hull House, a settlement house where the poor and immigrants could come for job training, day care, education, health care, and recreation in the city of Chicago. **4.** Notes should reflect harsh working conditions of the children of the poor. **5.** Possible answers: Furnishings—rocker, hall stand, etagere, stereoscope, tables and chairs, smoker's chair, gentleman's and lady's upholstered chairs, rustic furniture, gasolier, kerosene lamps, folding screen. Customs—calling cards, planting trees to mark special occasions, children barred from parlor, use of smoker's chair; Pastimes—croquet, lawn tennis, archery, bicycling, gardening, collecting and viewing stereographs, playing piano, reading, quilting, embroidery, needlepoint, making wax fruit and flower arrangements, baseball, bowling. **6.** Possible answers: Music—ragtime, blues, classical. Literature—work by Mark Twain, Stephen Crane, Hamlin Garland, Jack London, Kate Chopin,

and Louisa May Alcott. Sports—gymnastics, tennis, figure skating, golf, baseball, football, basketball, hockey. **7.** Use the following guidelines to evaluate charts: Is the material well-organized? Does the student include sufficient and meaningful points of comparison? Does the student include some similarities? Did students make good use of the research they did?

Activity 21
The Suffragists
1. Bushnell—opposed, women should be "the fair sex"; Stanton—supported, voting was a woman's right because she was a citizen; Milholland—supported, women would use the vote to "protect life"; Addams—supported, in order to protect and care for the home and children properly, women should be able to choose government officials; Lowe—supported, wage-earning women needed the vote for self-protection; Blackwell—supported, the Bible's Golden Rule should be applied: if men did not want taxation without representation, then they should not impose this on women; Women's Anti-Suffrage Association of Massachusetts—opposed, women's place is in the home and they do not need the vote. **2.** Students should list appropriate references. **3.** Notes should reflect information on suffrage movement. **4.** Possible notes: Stanton—clerks teased her by reading laws that denied basic rights to women; Addams—before she was seven years old, she had her first sight of the squalor of poverty in a small mill city; Rankin—Wrote "GO!" in her diary when she graduated from University of Montana in 1902. **5.** Possible images: suffragists, Rankin, Stanton, and Anthony. **6.** Openings should show an awareness of audience and an interesting use of research material. **7.** Use the following guidelines to evaluate tours: Is the material well-organized? Is it historically accurate? Does the writer demonstrate a good understanding of the issue and events surrounding it? Has the writer covered the topic thoroughly?

Activity 22
Overseas Expansion
1. Notes should include material covered in the Time Tour. **2.** Notes could include: areas gained by the United States in Pacific; movement of American forces and location of American military victories in Spanish-American War; length and location of Panama Canal. **3.** Alfred T. Mahan believed that the United States had the right to extend its influence around the globe, strengthen its navy, establish bases on major sea routes, and acquire colonies. **4.** Spanish-American War; building of Panama Canal **5.** Topics and messages should reflect understanding of American overseas expansion. **6.** You may wish to check first sketches. **7.** Use the following guidelines to evaluate cartoons: Is the topic and message historically accurate? Does the cartoon demonstrate an understanding of the events? Do the captions or written words go with the illustration? Is the cartoon well-executed from a visual standpoint?

Activity 23
World War I on the Home Front

1. Notes should include material covered in the Time Tour. **2.** Possible answers: "Europe in World War I" would show Americans which nations were Allies, which were Central Powers, and which were neutral. "The Western Front" would show where the Allied troops were fighting. These maps would help Americans at home understand the politics of the conflict and see where their relatives serving in the armed forces might be stationed. **3.** Possible answer: Rankin voted against World War I. **4.** Identity and point of view about the war should match. **5.** You may wish to check the list of five entries before students begin writing. **6.** Possible images: World War I poster, "Over There" song sheet, Jeannette Rankin, Woodrow Wilson **7.** Use the following guidelines to evaluate scrapbook: Did students include a variety of entries? Did students show creativity and skill in utilizing research material for the assignment? Is the material historically accurate?

Activity 24
The Jazz Age

1. Students should list appropriate references. **2.** Notes should cover information about jazz. **3.** Possible images: Louis Armstrong, jazz club. **4.** You may wish to review this description of the focus before students begin their research. **5.** Students should list two or three key words (could be general, as well as at least one address of a useful site. **6–7.** Use the following guidelines to evaluate the presentations: Is the information accurate? Is the presentation or-ganized in a logical way? Did the student show creativity in presenting the material?

Activity 25
The New Deal

1. Notes should reflect the information on the New Deal. **2.** Possible statements: It was a huge project involving several states; it provided many jobs; it helped millions of people by providing electric power. **3.** Possible answers: buried farmhouses, prevented good crops, hurt poor farmers, caused farmers to become migrant workers. **4.** Possible notes: He assembled a team of economic experts to create new policies and programs. He sent dozens of new bills to Congress to ease conditions caused by the Depression. **5.** Possible answers: the Dust Bowl, the Depression as a whole, the TVA project, the Civilian Conservation Corps, the Works Progress Administration, the National Recovery Administration, the Agricultural Adjustment Act, Social Security. **6.** Opening statements should be informative, persuasive, or catchy. **7.** Use the following guidelines to evaluate fireside chats: Is it appealing and persuasive? Does it reflect careful research? Is it well-organized and clearly presented?

Activity 26
A Global War

1. Possible events: German invasion of Poland in 1939; surrender of France to Germany; air raids on London; bombing of Pearl Harbor; entry of the United States into the war; internment of Japanese Americans; Soviets push Germans back from Leningrad; D-Day; surrender of Germany in 1945; Holocaust; atomic bomb dropped on Japan. **2.** Possible notes: Roosevelt—President when United States entered war; worked with Churchill and Stalin to end war; Yalta conference. Truman—Took over presidency during war; made decision to drop atomic bomb on Japan which ended the war. **3.** You might wish to check topic before students begin their research on the Internet. **4.** Students should list at least one key word and two addresses of useful sites. **5.** Use the following guidelines to evaluate outlines for television documentaries: Is the material historically and geographically accurate? Has the student organized the material in a logical and interesting way? Does the plan reflect skill in research and presentation? Is the plan focused?

Activity 27
The Cold War

1. Check to see that students set up their files for notes. **2.** Notes should reflect the CD-ROM information on the Cold War, including the audio and video material. **3.** Possible notes: People—Ho Chi Minh, Eisenhower, Kennedy, Johnson, Dulles, Students for a Democratic Society, Morse, King. Places—South Vietnam, North Vietnam, Southeast Asian peninsula. Events/Ideas—bombing raids, domino theory, Communist rule, marches, demonstrations, rallies, "Vietnamization," fall of South Vietnam. **4.** Possible question: Which President refused to invade China because it might start another world war? a. Eisenhower b. Truman c. Kennedy. (Truman) **5.** What famous monument did Maya Lin design? a. Vietnam Veterans Memorial b. Jefferson Memorial c. St. Louis Arch (Vietnam Veterans Memorial) **6.** Use the following guidelines to evaluate games: Do the questions cover different aspects of the Cold War? Do the questions demonstrate a good use of research skills? Did the student include answers?

Activity 28
Civil Rights

1. Possible notes: Oliver Brown: wanted daughter to attend white school near her home; Thurgood Marshall: Brown's lawyer who charged that segregated schools violated 14th amendment; John Davis: defended position of Southern states on school segregation. **2.** Notes should reflect CD-ROM information on the civil rights movement, including audio and video material. **3.** Marshall: successfully argued the case *Brown* v. *the Board of Education of Topeka* before the Supreme Court; Chavez: founded farm union for migrant workers; King: advocated nonviolent approach to work for civil rights. **4.** Work songs and spirituals became the freedom songs of the civil rights movement. In the late 1950s and 1960s, black and white Americans sang "We Shall Not Be Moved" and "We Shall Overcome." **5.** Possible images: Jackie Robinson, segregated school, Rosa Parks, civil rights march, Thurgood Marshall, Marshall and *Brown* v. *the Board of Education of Topeka* lawyers, Martin Luther King, Jr., John F. Kennedy. **6.** You may wish to check characters, setting, and historical details before students begin writing. **7.** Use the following guidelines to evaluate stories: Is the historical information accurate? Does the story include historical characters, an authentic setting, and accurate details? Does the story reflect skill and creativity in assessing and utilizing research?

Activity 29
A Changing World

1. Notes should reflect information about the end of the Cold War and the world today. **2.** Students should list key words and at least two addresses of useful sites. There should be excellent photos and even videoclips available on the Internet. **3.** You may wish to check the focus before students begin to work on their posters. **4.** Students should list at least five images to communicate their messages. **5.** Text should match images and message. Sketches should integrate text and images. **6.** Use the following guidelines to evaluate posters: Does the poster demonstrate an understanding of the events? Does the text go with the images? Is the poster well-executed from a visual standpoint?

Activity 30
Toward the Future

1. Possible notes: Design or Plan—one room with small root cellar and loft; Furniture—most made out of wood; settle, chairs, cradle, rope bed, ladder;

Food and Cooking—over open fire; gathered, grew or hunted food; Clothing—few clothes made of wool, linen, linsey-woolsey, or animal skins; Energy Sources—fire; Toys—few toys, carved or whittled; Entertainment—fiddle, one or two books. **2.** Possible notes: Design or Plan—ranch house identical to others in community, five or six rooms with a garage or carport, maybe a patio; Furniture—manufactured furniture in every room; Appliances—electric stoves, refrigerators, toasters, mixers, radios, phonographs, televisions, washer/dryers, freezers; Food and Cooking—frozen foods cooked on stove; Clothing—more clothes, often following fads such as full circle skirts; Energy Sources—electricity, coal, oil, gas; Toys—sports equipment, hula hoop, other plastic items from Play-Doh to Barbie; Entertainment—television, radio, phonograph, books, magazines, newspapers; Communication—telephone, television. **3.** Possible answers: Similarities—some kind of kitchen, chairs, toys; Differences—might have a computer, VCR, CD player, bins for recycling, fax machine, microwave. **4.** Notes should include information about new technology and concern about the environment. **5.** Check to see that students include new topics and cover some of the same topics as in questions 1 and 2. Use the following guidelines to evaluate descriptions and plans: Has the student included information about most of the topics listed? Has the student shown imagination? Has the student taken into consideration the issues and technological advances of today?

Activity 31
Civics Overview: American Democracy

1. Notes should reflect information about the branches of the national government. **2.** Students should choose one of the branches. **3.** Students should list at least two addresses of useful sites. **4.** You may wish to check these ideas before students create their virtual tour outlines. **5.** Use the following guidelines to evaluate outlines for virtual tours: Does the outline demonstrate an understanding of the branch the student chose? Does it reflect skill and creativity in assessing and utilizing research? Does the construction of the virtual tour show an understanding of how pages on the World Wide Web work?

TIME TOUR CONTENTS

Following is a detailed outline of the contents of the Time Tour.

MAPS

The *American Heritage® History of the United States* CD-ROM includes the following maps from Prentice Hall's *The American Nation*.

Unit 1
A Meeting of Different Worlds
Hunters Reach the Americas
Native American Culture Areas
Great Civilizations of the Americas
Spain in the Americas
The New England Colonies
The Middle Colonies
The Southern Colonies

Unit 2
From Revolution to Republic
The French and Indian War
North America in 1763
The Revolutionary War, 1776–1777
Burgoyne's March to Saratoga
The War in the West
The War in the South
North America in 1783
Claims to Western Lands
The Northwest Territory

Unit 3
The New Republic
The Louisiana Purchase
Lewis and Clark Cross the Continental Divide
The Barbary States
Land Lost by Indians
The War of 1812
Early Roads West
Major Canals

Unit 4
An Expanding Nation
Election of 1828
Indian Removal
Oregon Country
Independence for Texas
Trails to the West
War with Mexico
Growth of the United States to 1853
Products of the North

Unit 5
The Nation Torn Apart
Missouri Compromise
Choosing Sides
The Final Battles
Election of 1876

Unit 6
Reshaping the Nation
The Indians Retreat
Opening the West

Unit 7
A New Role in the World
The United States Expands in the Pacific
The Spanish-American War
The Panama Canal
Europe in World War I
The Western Front
Europe After World War I

Unit 8
Prosperity, Depression, and War
Tennessee Valley Authority
The Dust Bowl
Aggression in Europe

Unit 9
The Nation Today and Tomorrow
Eastern Europe After the Cold War
The Caribbean and Central America
The Middle East

Library
The United States: Satellite
The United States: Political
The United States: Physical

IMAGE LIBRARY

The following pictures are available in the Image Library, which is accessed from the Report Maker. Students can select and attach images from the library to their reports.

Presidents
George Washington
Washington crossing the Delaware
John Adams
Thomas Jefferson
James Madison
James Monroe
John Quincy Adams
Andrew Jackson, Battle of New Orleans
Andrew Jackson
Martin Van Buren
William Henry Harrison
John Tyler
James K. Polk
Zachary Taylor
Millard Fillmore
Franklin Pierce
James Buchanan
Emancipation Proclamation
  (Abraham Lincoln)
Abraham Lincoln
Andrew Johnson
Ulysses S. Grant
Rutherford B. Hayes
James A. Garfield
Chester A. Arthur
Grover Cleveland
Benjamin Harrison
William McKinley
Theodore Roosevelt and Rough Riders
Theodore Roosevelt
William Howard Taft
Woodrow Wilson
Warren G. Harding
Calvin Coolidge
Herbert C. Hoover
Franklin D. Roosevelt
  with Stalin and Churchill
Franklin D. Roosevelt
Harry S. Truman
Dwight D. Eisenhower
General Eisenhower in France, 1944
John F. Kennedy
Presidents Richard M. Nixon
  and John F. Kennedy
Lyndon B. Johnson
Richard M. Nixon
Gerald R. Ford
Jimmy Carter
Ronald W. Reagan

George H.W. Bush
William J. Clinton

History Makers
Christopher Columbus
John Smith
Pocahontas
William Penn
Anne Hutchinson
Benjamin Franklin
Benjamin Banneker
Daniel Boone
Patrick Henry
Abigail Adams
Phillis Wheatley
Alexander Hamilton
John Marshall
Tecumseh
The death of Tecumseh
Sequoyah
Sacajawea with Lewis and Clark
Henry Clay
Sam Houston
George Catlin
Robert E. Lee
Robert E. Lee surrenders at Appomattox
Harriet Beecher Stowe
Uncle Tom's Cabin
Elizabeth Cady Stanton
  and Susan B. Anthony
Frederick Douglass
Harriet Tubman (2 pictures)
Clara Barton
Hiram Revels
Emily Dickinson
Chief Joseph
Andrew Carnegie
Mark Twain
Winslow Homer
Cotton Pickers by Winslow Homer
Alfred T. Mahan
Thomas Edison
Samuel Gompers
Ida Tarbell
Jane Addams
Henry Ford
Orville and Wilbur Wright
W.E.B. Du Bois
Jeannette Rankin
Eleanor Roosevelt
Babe Ruth

Louis Armstrong
Langston Hughes
Charles Lindbergh
Thurgood Marshall
Thurgood Marshall and *Brown* v.
  Board of Education of Topeka lawyers
Cesar Chavez
Martin Luther King, Jr.
Sandra Day O'Connor
Maya Lin

General

Crusaders
Navajo jar
Inuit bear mask
Aztec stone calendar
Vasco da Gama
Pilgrims leave England
Fur trading
Buffalo hunt
Peter Minuit buys Manhattan
Colonists at town meeting
John Winthrop
Slave trade
Whaling
Death of General Braddock
Stamp Act cartoon
King George III
Boston Massacre
Boston Tea Party
Revolutionary motto
Battle of Bunker Hill
Patrick Henry
Battle of Lexington
Presentation of Declaration of Independence
Fife and drum players, 1776
Cornwallis surrenders
President Washington's Cabinet
Bank of the United States
Enslaved African Americans on a plantation
Slave auction
Mill, early 1800s
The U.S.S. *Constitution*
Francis Scott Key
Westward expansion
Abolition slogan
Erie Canal
Erie Railroad
Nat Turner
Sojourner Truth
The Alamo
Trail of Tears
Mexican War
Commodore Perry in Japan
Dred Scott

John Brown
Battle of Gettysburg
Furling the Confederate flag
African American soldiers (Civil War)
African American congressmen (Reconstruction)
African Americans vote (Reconstruction)
Pioneers
Cowboy
Woman's Christian Temperance Union march
Alexander Graham Bell
Colonel George Custer
"Remember the Maine!"
Panama Canal
Cotton pickers, around 1907
Hungarian immigrants, around 1910
New York City, late 1800s
Paperboy, 1910
Readers, late 1800s
Suffragists, around 1912
Woman at work, around 1912
World War I poster
World War I
"Over There" song sheet
Jazz club
Clarence Darrow
Zora Neale Hurston
Jim Thorpe
Migrants, 1930s
WPA
Unemployed, 1937
Wizard of Oz
Gone With the Wind
Pearl Harbor
Japanese-American internment
Concentration camp survivors
Iwo Jima
Anti-Communist poster
Bomb shelter, 1950s
Jackie Robinson
Segregated school
Rosa Parks
Civil rights march, 1968
Equal Rights Amendment march, 1971
Camp David Accords
Star Wars
Space walk, 1984
Environmentalists protest, 1988
Fall of the Berlin Wall, 1989
Yitzhak Rabin and Yasir Arafat
Carl Lewis and Ben Johnson
Michael Jordan
General Colin Powell
New citizens

VIDEO FOOTAGE

The following video footage can be accessed by clicking the play buttons beneath the video windows that appear as you scroll through the *American Heritage® History of the United States* CD-ROM.

Subject	Time
Pueblo hoop dance	15 seconds
Immigrants at Ellis Island	40 seconds
Wilbur and Orville Wright, early flight	20 seconds
Charlie Chaplin	20 seconds
World War I	40 seconds
Thomas Edison	24 seconds
Automobile assembly line	18 seconds
Model T Ford on the road	10 seconds
Theodore Roosevelt	27 seconds
Charleston (1920s dance)	23 seconds
Suffragists march and women vote	35 seconds
Prohibition	30 seconds
Babe Didrickson (golf)	12 seconds
Babe Ruth	20 seconds
Charles Lindbergh	26 seconds
Red Grange and Knute Rockne	28 seconds
Jesse Owens	25 seconds
Great Depression	34 seconds
Dust Bowl, 1930s	50 seconds
Franklin D. Roosevelt: Speech after Pearl Harbor	55 seconds
D-Day: Troops landing	40 seconds
Harry Truman: Speech on Korean War	32 seconds
Kitchen, 1950s	31 seconds
Suburbs, 1950s	16 seconds
Drive-in movie, 1950s	25 seconds
Early television	30 seconds
Lucille Ball on *Bob Hope Show*	31 seconds
Hula hoop and yo-yo craze	20 seconds
John F. Kennedy inaugural speech	58 seconds
Apollo 11 launch	40 seconds
Martin Luther King: "I Have a Dream" speech	2 min 41 seconds
Freedom Riders	40 seconds
Jackie Robinson	18 seconds
Muhammad Ali	25 seconds
Vietnam War	28 seconds
Jimmy Carter	30 seconds

★ ★ ★ ★ ★ ★ ★ ★ ★ ★ ★ ★ ★ ★ ★

SOFTWARE LICENSE AGREEMENT AND LIMITED WARRANTY

READ THE FOLLOWING TERMS AND CONDITIONS CAREFULLY BEFORE OPENING THE SEALED DISK PACKAGE. THIS LEGAL DOCUMENT IS AN AGREEMENT BETWEEN YOU AND PRENTICE-HALL, INC. (THE "COMPANY"). BY OPENING THE SEALED DISK PACKAGE, YOU ARE AGREEING TO BE BOUND BY THESE TERMS AND CONDITIONS. IF YOU DO NOT AGREE WITH THESE TERMS AND CONDITIONS, DO NOT OPEN THE DISK PACKAGE. PROMPTLY RETURN THE UNOPENED DISK PACKAGE AND ALL ACCOMPANYING ITEMS TO THE PLACE YOU OBTAINED THEM FOR A FULL REFUND OF ANY SUMS YOU HAVE PAID.

1. GRANT OF LICENSE: In consideration of your payment of the license fee, which is part of the price you paid for this product, and your agreement to abide by the terms and conditions of this Agreement, the COMPANY grants to you a nonexclusive right to use and display the copy of the software program entitled "*American Heritage*® History of the United States CD-ROM" (hereinafter "the SOFTWARE") on a single computer (i.e., with a single CPU) at a single location so long as you comply with the terms of this Agreement. The COMPANY reserves all rights not expressly granted to you under this Agreement.

2. OWNERSHIP OF SOFTWARE: You own only the magnetic or physical media (the enclosed disks) on which the SOFTWARE is recorded or fixed, but the COMPANY retains all the rights, title, and ownership to the SOFTWARE recorded on the original disk copy(ies) and all subsequent copies of the SOFTWARE, regardless of the form or media on which the original or other copies may exist. This license is not a sale of the original SOFTWARE or any copy to you.

3. COPY RESTRICTIONS: The SOFTWARE and the accompanying printed materials and user manual (the "Documentation") are the subject of copyright. You may not copy the Documentation or the SOFTWARE, except that you may make a single copy of the SOFTWARE for backup or archival purposes only. You may be held legally responsible for any copying or copyright infringement that is caused or encouraged by your failure to abide by the terms of this restriction.

4. USE RESTRICTIONS: You may not network the SOFTWARE or otherwise use it on more than one computer or computer terminal at the same time. You may physically transfer the SOFTWARE from one computer to another provided that the SOFTWARE is used on only one computer at a time. You may not distribute copies of the SOFTWARE or the Documentation to others. You may not reverse engineer, disassemble, decompile, modify, adapt, translate, or create derivative works based on the SOFTWARE or the Documentation without the prior written consent of the COMPANY.

5. TRANSFER RESTRICTIONS: The SOFTWARE is licensed only to you and may not be transferred to anyone else without the prior written consent of the COMPANY. Any unauthorized transfer of the SOFTWARE shall result in the immediate termination of this Agreement.

6. TERMINATION: This license is effective until terminated. This license will terminate automatically without notice from the COMPANY and become null and void if you fail to comply with any provisions or limitations of this license. Upon termination, you shall destroy the Documentation and all copies of the SOFTWARE. All provisions of this Agreement as to warranties, limitation of liability, remedies or damages, and our ownership rights shall survive termination.

7. MISCELLANEOUS: This Agreement shall be construed in accordance with the laws of the United States of America and the State of New York and shall benefit the COMPANY, its affiliates, and assignees.

8. LIMITED WARRANTY AND DISCLAIMER OF WARRANTY: The COMPANY warrants that the SOFTWARE, when properly used in accordance with the Documentation, will operate in substantial conformity with the description of the SOFTWARE set forth in the Documentation. The COMPANY does not warrant that the SOFTWARE will meet your requirements or that the operation of the SOFTWARE will be uninterrupted or error-free. The COMPANY warrants that the media on which the SOFTWARE is delivered shall be free from defects in materials and workmanship under normal use for a period of thirty (30) days from the date of your purchase. Your only remedy and the COMPANY's only obligation under these limited warranties is, at the COMPANY's option, return of the warranted item for a refund of any amounts paid by you or replacement of the item. Any replacement of SOFTWARE or media under the warranties shall not extend the original warranty period. The limited warranty set forth above shall not apply to any SOFTWARE that the COMPANY determines in good faith has been subject to misuse, neglect, improper installation, repair, alteration, or damage by you. EXCEPT FOR THE EXPRESSED WARRANTIES SET FORTH ABOVE, THE COMPANY DISCLAIMS ALL WARRANTIES, EXPRESS OR IMPLIED, INCLUDING WITHOUT LIMITATION, THE IMPLIED WARRANTIES OF MERCHANTABILITY AND FITNESS FOR A PARTICULAR PURPOSE. EXCEPT FOR THE EXPRESS WARRANTY SET FORTH ABOVE, THE COMPANY DOES NOT WARRANT, GUARANTEE, OR MAKE ANY REPRESENTATION REGARDING THE USE OR THE RESULTS OF THE USE OF THE SOFTWARE IN TERMS OF ITS CORRECTNESS, ACCURACY, RELIABILITY, CURRENTNESS, OR OTHERWISE.

IN NO EVENT SHALL THE COMPANY OR ITS EMPLOYEES, AGENTS, SUPPLIERS, OR CONTRACTORS BE LIABLE FOR ANY INCIDENTAL, INDIRECT, SPECIAL, OR CONSEQUENTIAL DAMAGES ARISING OUT OF OR IN CONNECTION WITH THE LICENSE GRANTED UNDER THIS AGREEMENT, OR FOR LOSS OF USE, LOSS OF DATA, LOSS OF INCOME OR PROFIT, OR OTHER LOSSES SUSTAINED AS A RESULT OF INJURY TO ANY PERSON, OR LOSS OF OR DAMAGE TO PROPERTY, OR CLAIMS OF THIRD PARTIES, EVEN IF THE COMPANY OR AN AUTHORIZED REPRESENTATIVE OF THE COMPANY HAS BEEN ADVISED OF THE POSSIBILITY OF SUCH DAMAGES. IN NO EVENT SHALL LIABILITY OF THE COMPANY FOR DAMAGES WITH RESPECT TO THE SOFTWARE EXCEED THE AMOUNTS ACTUALLY PAID BY YOU, IF ANY, FOR THE SOFTWARE.

SOME JURISDICTIONS DO NOT ALLOW THE LIMITATION OF IMPLIED WARRANTIES OR LIABILITY FOR INCIDENTAL, INDIRECT, SPECIAL OR CONSEQUENTIAL DAMAGES, SO THE ABOVE LIMITATIONS MAY NOT ALWAYS APPLY. THE WARRANTIES IN THIS AGREEMENT GIVE YOU SPECIFIC LEGAL RIGHTS AND YOU MAY ALSO HAVE OTHER RIGHTS THAT VARY IN ACCORDANCE WITH LOCAL LAW.

ACKNOWLEDGMENT

YOU ACKNOWLEDGE THAT YOU HAVE READ THIS AGREEMENT, UNDERSTAND IT, AND AGREE TO BE BOUND BY ITS TERMS AND CONDITIONS. YOU ALSO AGREE THAT THIS AGREEMENT IS THE COMPLETE AND EXCLUSIVE STATEMENT OF THE AGREEMENT BETWEEN YOU AND THE COMPANY AND SUPERSEDES ALL PROPOSALS OR PRIOR AGREEMENTS, ORAL OR WRITTEN, AND ANY OTHER COMMUNICATIONS BETWEEN YOU AND THE COMPANY OR ANY REPRESENTATIVE OF THE COMPANY RELATING TO THE SUBJECT MATTER OF THIS AGREEMENT.

Should you have any questions concerning this agreement or if you wish to contact the COMPANY for any reason, please contact in writing: Prentice Hall, School Division, One Lake Street, Upper Saddle River, NJ 07458 attn: Social Studies